Non-verbal Reasoning
Progress Papers 2

Rebecca Brant

Schofield & Sims

Introduction

The **Non-verbal Reasoning Progress Papers** provide structured activities that increase in difficulty throughout the series, developing your knowledge and skills in non-verbal reasoning. Use the books to prepare for school entrance examinations and to improve your non-verbal reasoning skills.

How to use this book

There are seven papers in this book. Each contains 50 questions, divided by topic into sets of five. The 10 most common types of non-verbal reasoning question are featured in each test paper.

Read through the **Example questions** on pages 4 and 5. Work out why each answer given is correct and then move on to the test papers. Each question in the book is a multiple-choice question. Look closely at the question and its answer options, then draw a ring around the letter option you think is correct.

A single paper may take between 45 and 75 minutes to complete, and you might need two or more sessions to complete one paper.

- For exam preparation, revision and all-round practice, you may choose to work through the papers in numerical order. Once you have completed a paper, ask a teacher, parent or adult helper to correct any mistakes and to explain where you went wrong.

- To practise a topic that you find particularly challenging, you can concentrate on one area and use topic-based material to proceed through the exercises in order of difficulty.

Answers

The answers to all the questions in this book can be found in a pull-out section in the middle. You (or an adult) should use this to mark your work at the end of each paper. You will receive one mark for each correct answer, giving you a total mark out of 50 for every paper. Take time to learn and remember why the answer given is correct.

Use the **Progress chart** at the back of this book to record your marks and measure progress.

Downloads

Free downloads are available from the Schofield & Sims website (www.schofieldandsims.co.uk/free-downloads), including extra practice material.

Published by Schofield & Sims Ltd
Dogley Mill, Fenay Bridge, Huddersfield HD8 0NQ, UK
Telephone 01484 607080
www.schofieldandsims.co.uk
First published in 2016
This edition copyright © Schofield & Sims Ltd, 2018
Author: Rebecca Brant
Rebecca Brant has asserted her moral rights under the Copyright, Designs and Patents Act, 1988, to be identified as the author of this work.
British Library Cataloguing in Publication Data
A catalogue record for this book is available from the British Library.

Design by **Oxford Designers & Illustrators**
Cover design by **Ledgard Jepson Ltd**
Printed in the UK by **Page Bros (Norwich) Ltd**
ISBN 978 07217 1461 5

Contents

Note for parents, tutors, teachers and other adult helpers
A pull-out answers section (pages A1 to A12) appears in the centre of this book, between pages 28 and 29 (Paper 11). This provides answers to all the questions, along with guidance on marking the papers. Remove the pull-out section before the child begins working through the practice papers. The child may have access to a spare piece of paper for the nets of cubes questions if needed.

Example questions

Similarities

Which picture on the right belongs to the group on the left? Circle the letter.

Example

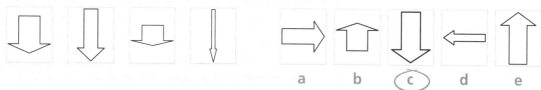

Analogies

Which of the five pictures on the right goes with the third one to make a pair like the two on the left? Circle the letter.

Example

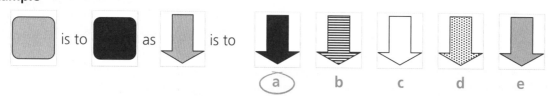

Matrices

Which picture on the right best fits into the space in the grid? Circle the letter.

Example

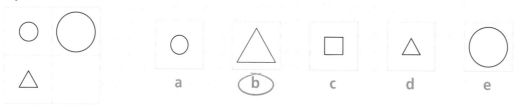

Hidden pictures

In which picture on the right is the picture on the left hidden? Circle the letter.

Example

Odd ones out

Which picture is the odd one out? Circle the letter.

Example

Reflected pictures

Which picture on the right is a reflection of the picture on the left? Circle the letter.

Example

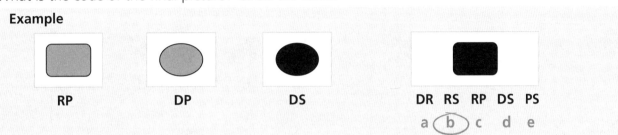

Codes

What is the code of the final picture? Circle the letter.

Example

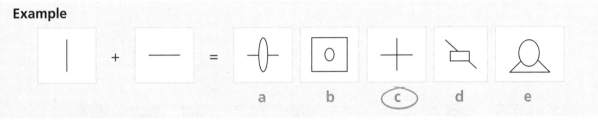

Combined pictures

Which picture on the right can be made by combining the first two pictures? Circle the letter.

Example

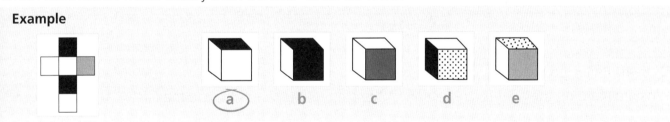

Nets of cubes

Which cube can be made exactly from the net? Circle the letter.

Example

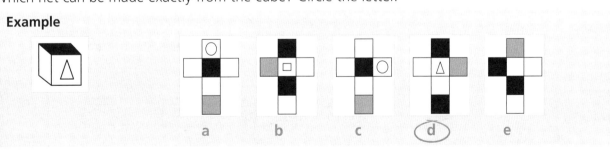

Which net can be made exactly from the cube? Circle the letter.

Example

Series

Which picture on the right fits in the empty space? Circle the letter.

Example

START HERE

Q. 1–5 Series

Which picture on the right fits in the empty space? Circle the letter.

1

      a   b   c   d   e   1

2

      a   b   c   d   e   2

3

      a   b   c   d   e   3

4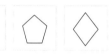

      a   b   c   d   e   4

5

      a   b   c   d   e   5

Q. 6–10 Reflected pictures

Which picture on the right is a reflection of the picture on the left? Circle the letter.

6

      a   b   c   d   e   6

7

      a   b   c   d   e   7

8

      a   b   c   d   e   8

MARK

MARK
✓ OR ✗

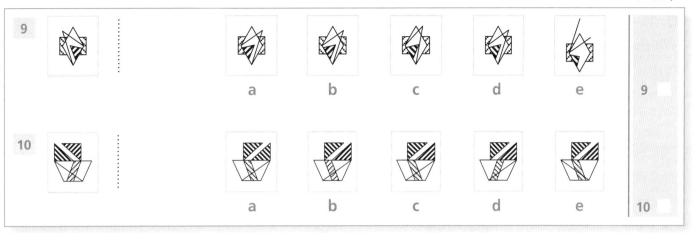

9

10

Q. 11–15 Similarities

Which picture on the right belongs to the group on the left? Circle the letter.

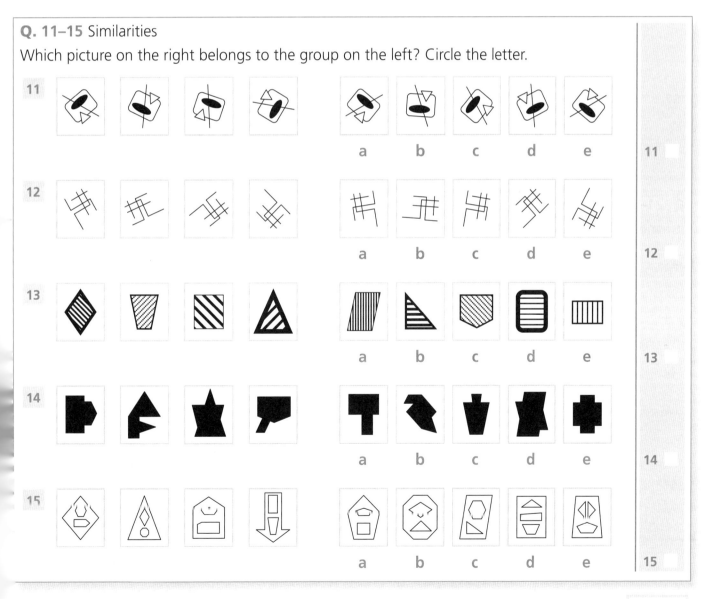

11

12

13

14

15

MARK

MARK
✓ OR ✗

Q. 16–20 Odd ones out

Which picture is the odd one out? Circle the letter.

16

    a   b   c   d   e   16

17

    a   b   c   d   e   17

18

    a   b   c   d   e   18

19

    a   b   c   d   e   19

20

    a   b   c   d   e   20

Q. 21–25 Hidden pictures

In which picture on the right is the picture on the left hidden? Circle the letter.

21

                       a   b   c   d   e   21

22

                       a   b   c   d   e   22

23

                       a   b   c   d   e   23

MARK

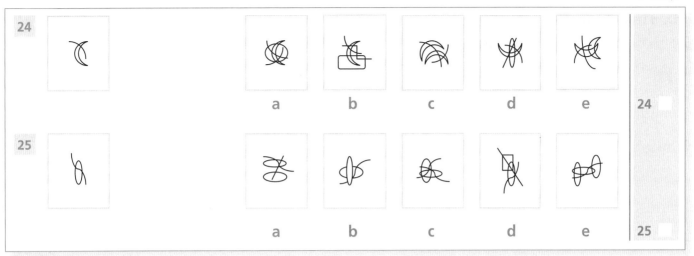

MARK
✓ OR ✗

24 | 24
25 | 25

Q. 26–30 Analogies

Which of the five pictures on the right goes with the third one to make a pair like the two on the left? Circle the letter.

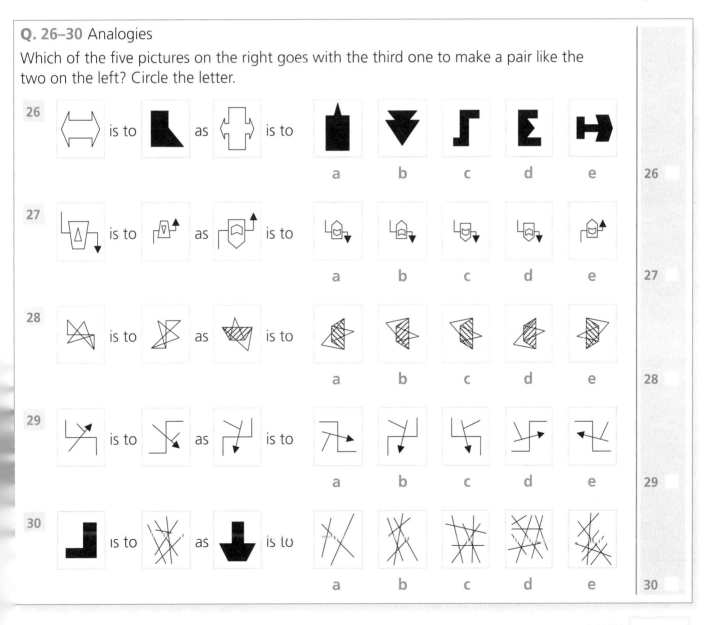

MARK
✓ OR ✗

Q. 31–35 Matrices

Which picture on the right best fits into the space in the grid? Circle the letter.

31

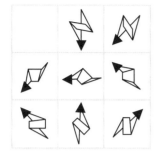

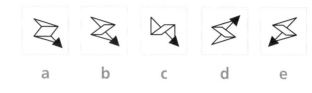

a   b   c   d   e

31

32

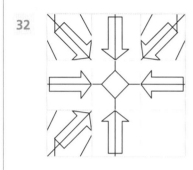

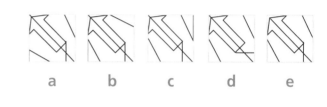

a   b   c   d   e

32

33

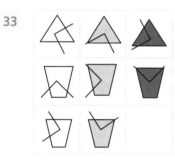

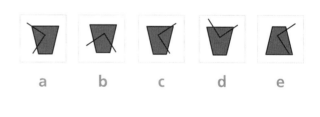

a   b   c   d   e

33

34

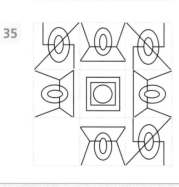

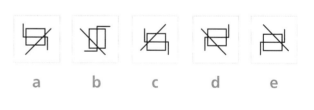

a   b   c   d   e

34

35

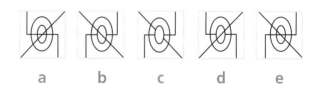

a   b   c   d   e

35

MARK

MARK
✓ OR ✗

Q. 36–40 Codes

What is the code of the final picture? Circle the letter.

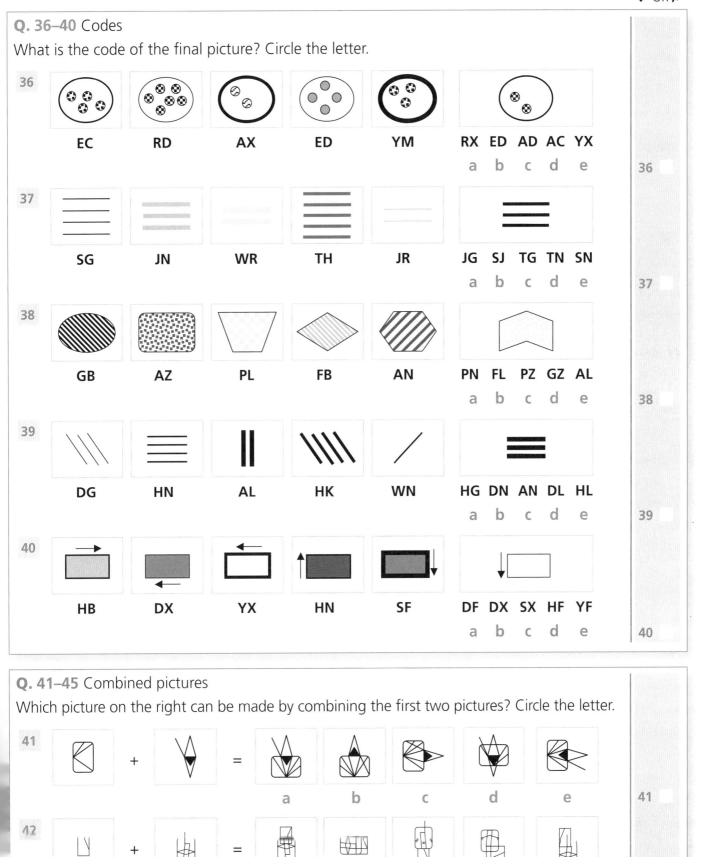

36

EC RD AX ED YM

RX ED AD AC YX
a   b   c   d   e

37

SG JN WR TH JR

JG SJ TG TN SN
a   b   c   d   e

38

GB AZ PL FB AN

PN FL PZ GZ AL
a   b   c   d   e

39

DG HN AL HK WN

HG DN AN DL HL
a   b   c   d   e

40

HB DX YX HN SF

DF DX SX HF YF
a   b   c   d   e

36

37

38

39

40

Q. 41–45 Combined pictures

Which picture on the right can be made by combining the first two pictures? Circle the letter.

41

a   b   c   d   e

41

42

a   b   c   d   e

42

MARK

MARK
✓ OR ✗

Which picture on the right can be made by combining the first two pictures? Circle the letter.

43 + =

                                          a   b   c   d   e   **43**

44 + =

                                          a   b   c   d   e   **44**

45 + =

                                          a   b   c   d   e   **45**

Q. 46–50 Nets of cubes

Which net can be made exactly from the cube? Circle the letter.

46

                                        a   b   c   d   e   **46**

47

                                        a   b   c   d   e   **47**

Which cube can be made exactly from the net? Circle the letter.

48

                                        a   b   c   d   e   **48**

49

                                        a   b   c   d   e   **49**

50

                                        a   b   c   d   e   **50**

MARK

END OF TEST

PAPER 8 TOTAL MARK

Paper 9

START HERE

MARK ✓ OR ✗

Q. 1–5 Reflected pictures

Which picture on the right is a reflection of the picture on the left? Circle the letter.

1
a b c d e 1

2
a b c d e 2

3
a b c d e 3

4
a b c d e 4

5
a b c d e 5

Q. 6–10 Similarities

Which picture on the right belongs to the group on the left? Circle the letter.

6
a b c d e 6

7
a b c d e 7

8
a b c d e 8

MARK

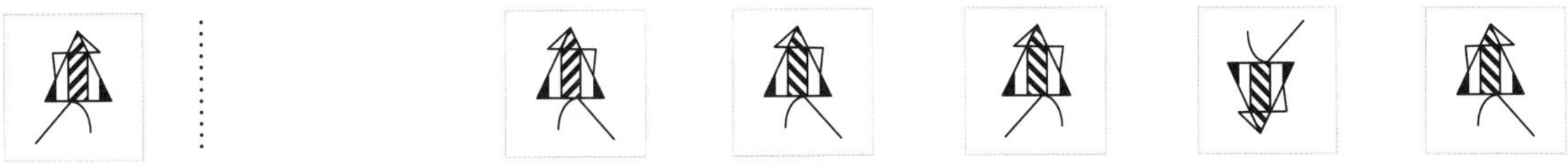

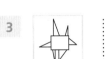

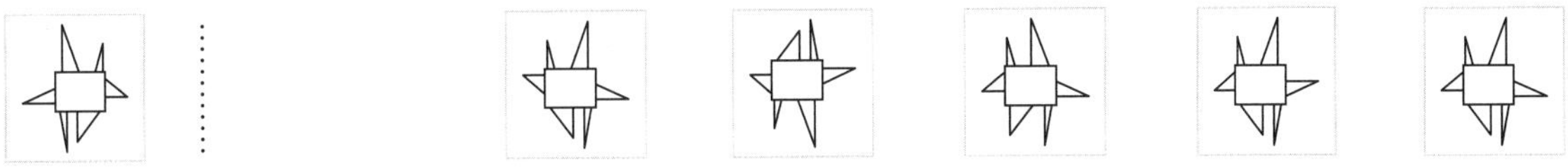

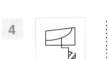

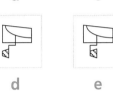

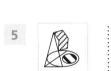

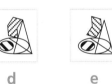

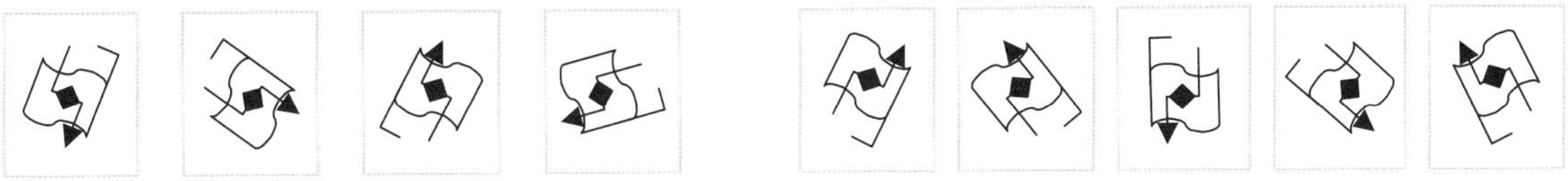

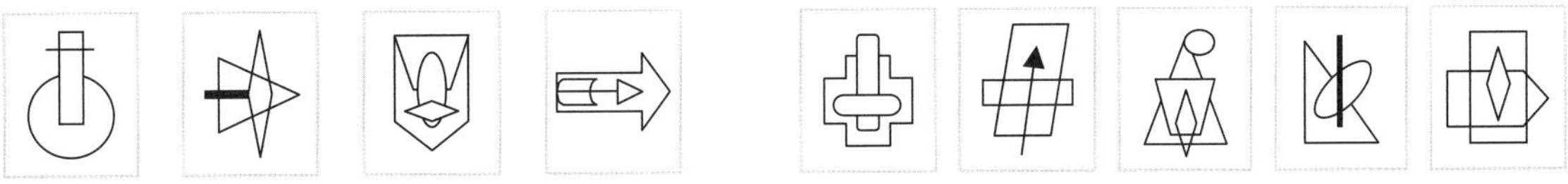

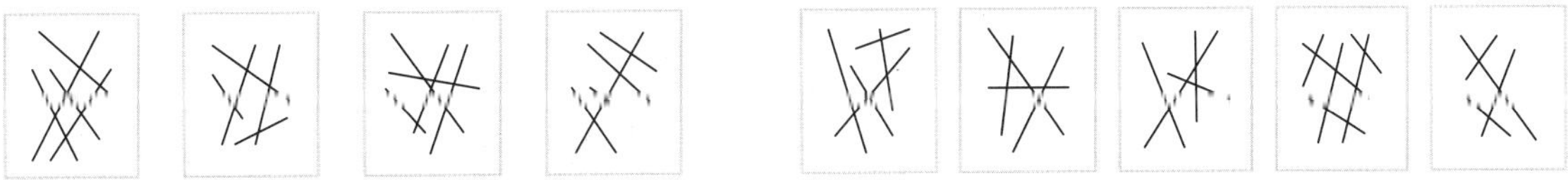

MARK
✓ OR ✗

Which picture on the right belongs to the group on the left? Circle the letter.

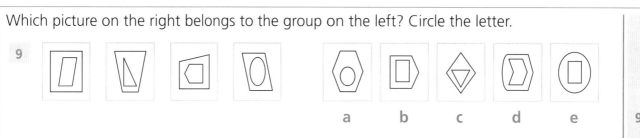

9

a   b   c   d   e   9

10

a   b   c   d   e   10

Q. 11–15 Odd ones out

Which picture is the odd one out? Circle the letter.

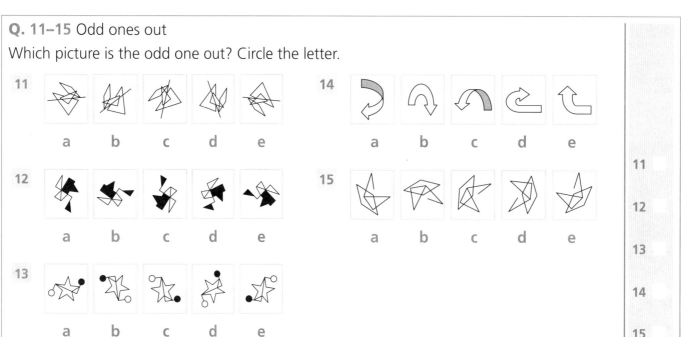

11

a   b   c   d   e

14

a   b   c   d   e

11

12

a   b   c   d   e

15

a   b   c   d   e

12

13

13

a   b   c   d   e

14

15

Q. 16–20 Hidden pictures

In which picture on the right is the picture on the left hidden? Circle the letter.

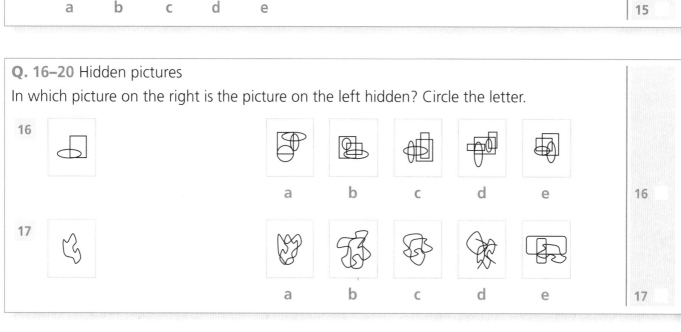

16

a   b   c   d   e   16

17

a   b   c   d   e   17

MARK

MARK
✓ OR ✗

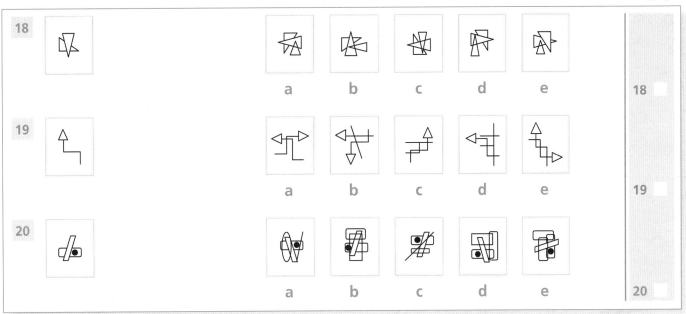

18

19

20

Q. 21–25 Analogies

Which of the five pictures on the right goes with the third one to make a pair like the two on the left? Circle the letter.

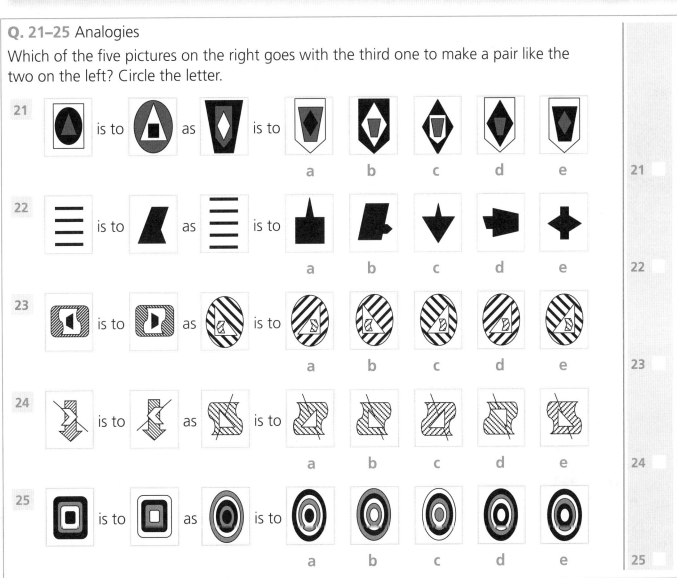

21

22

23

24

25

MARK

Q. 26–30 Matrices

Which picture on the right best fits into the space in the grid? Circle the letter.

26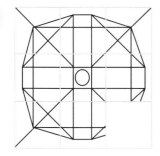

  a   b   c   d   e

26

27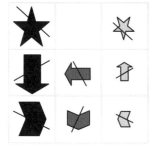

  a   b   c   d   e

27

28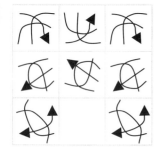

  a   b   c   d   e

28

29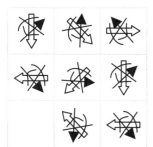

  a   b   c   d   e

29

30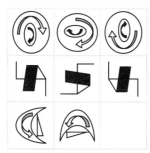

  a   b   c   d   e

30

MARK

Schofield & Sims • Non-verbal Reasoning Progress Papers 2

MARK
✓ OR ✗

Q. 31–35 Codes

What is the code of the final picture? Circle the letter.

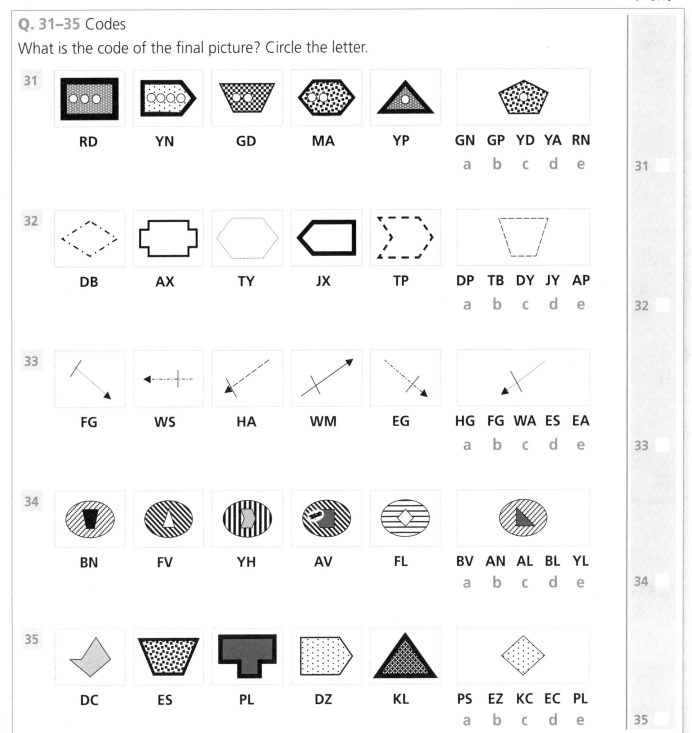

31

RD   YN   GD   MA   YP

GN   GP   YD   YA   RN
a   b   c   d   e

31 ☐

32

DB   AX   TY   JX   TP

DP   TB   DY   JY   AP
a   b   c   d   e

32 ☐

33

FG   WS   HA   WM   EG

HG   FG   WA   ES   EA
a   b   c   d   e

33 ☐

34

BN   FV   YH   AV   FL

BV   AN   AL   BL   YL
a   b   c   d   e

34 ☐

35

DC   ES   PL   DZ   KL

PS   EZ   KC   EC   PL
a   b   c   d   e

35 ☐

MARK ☐

MARK
✓ OR ✗

Q. 36–40 Combined pictures

Which picture on the right can be made by combining the first two pictures? Circle the letter.

36 + =
  a b c d e 36

37 + =
  a b c d e 37

38 + =
  a b c d e 38

39 + =
  a b c d e 39

40 + =
  a b c d e 40

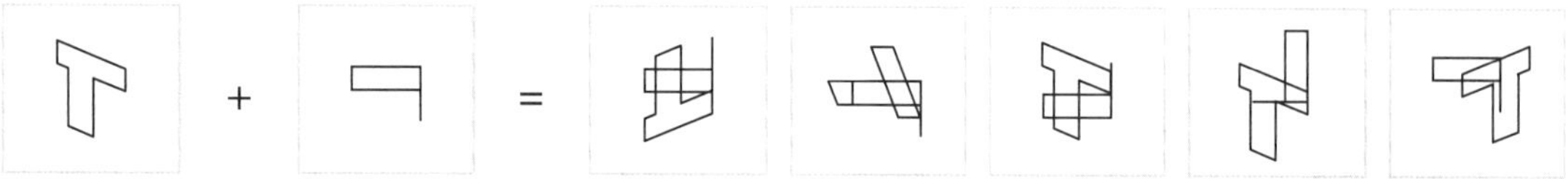

Q. 41–45 Nets of cubes

Which net can be made exactly from the cube? Circle the letter.

41
  a b c d e 41

42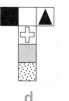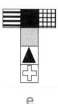
  a b c d e 42

MARK

Schofield & Sims • Non-verbal Reasoning Progress Papers 2

MARK
✓ OR ✗

Which cube can be made exactly from the net? Circle the letter.

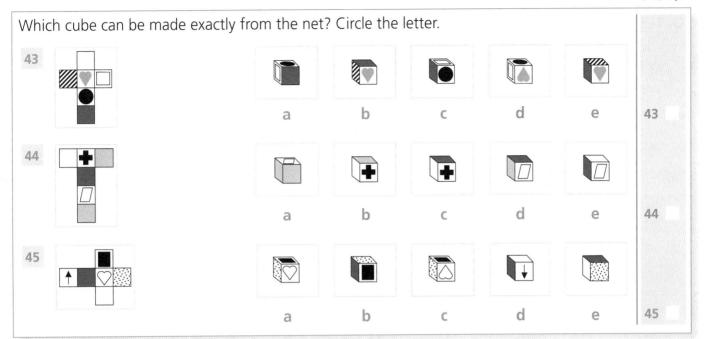

	a	b	c	d	e	
43						43
44						44
45						45

Q. 46–50 Series

Which picture on the right fits in the empty space? Circle the letter.

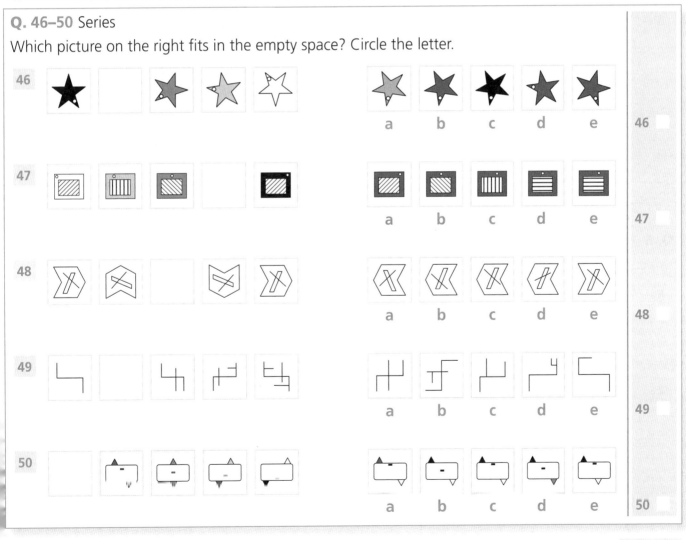

	a	b	c	d	e	
46						46
47						47
48						48
49						49
50						50

MARK

PAPER 9 TOTAL MARK

END OF TEST

START HERE

MARK
✓ OR ✗

Q. 1–5 Similarities
Which picture on the right belongs to the group on the left? Circle the letter.

1

a   b   c   d   e   1

2

a   b   c   d   e   2

3

a   b   c   d   e   3

4

a   b   c   d   e   4

5

a   b   c   d   e   5

Q. 6–10 Odd ones out
Which picture is the odd one out? Circle the letter.

6

a   b   c   d   e   6

9

a   b   c   d   e   7

7

a   b   c   d   e   8

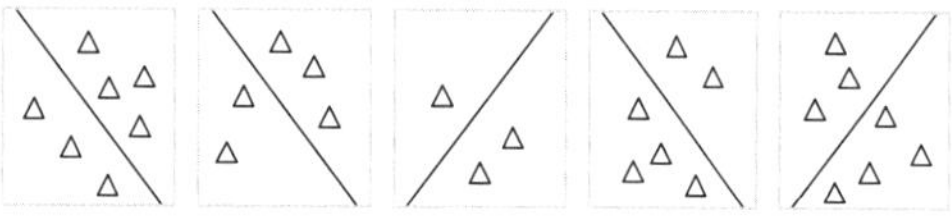

10

a   b   c   d   e   9

8

a   b   c   d   e   10

MARK

MARK
✓ OR ✗

Q. 11–15 Hidden pictures

In which picture on the right is the picture on the left hidden? Circle the letter.

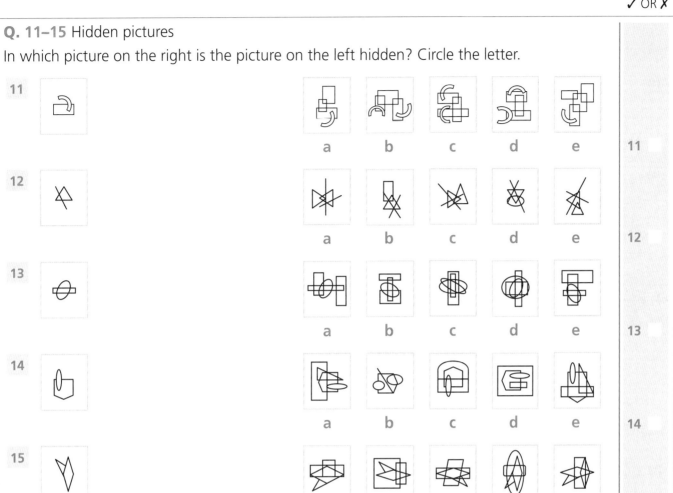

	a	b	c	d	e
11						11
12						12
13						13
14						14
15						15

Q. 16–20 Analogies

Which of the five pictures on the right goes with the third one to make a pair like the two on the left? Circle the letter.

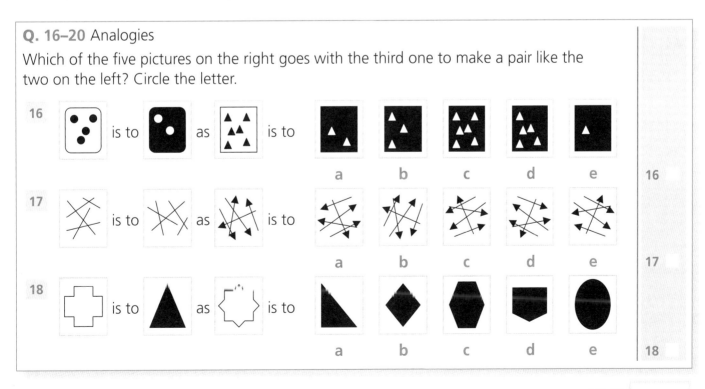

16

17

18

MARK

MARK
✓ OR ✗

Which of the five pictures on the right goes with the third one to make a pair like the two on the left? Circle the letter.

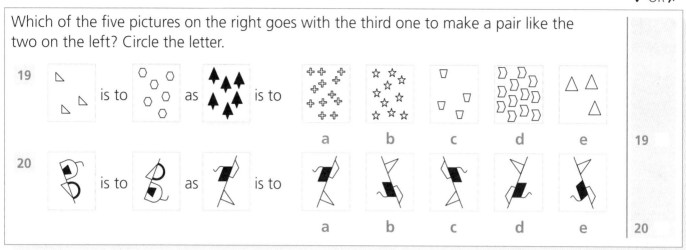

a   b   c   d   e   19

a   b   c   d   e   20

Q. 21–25 Matrices

Which picture on the right best fits into the space in the grid? Circle the letter.

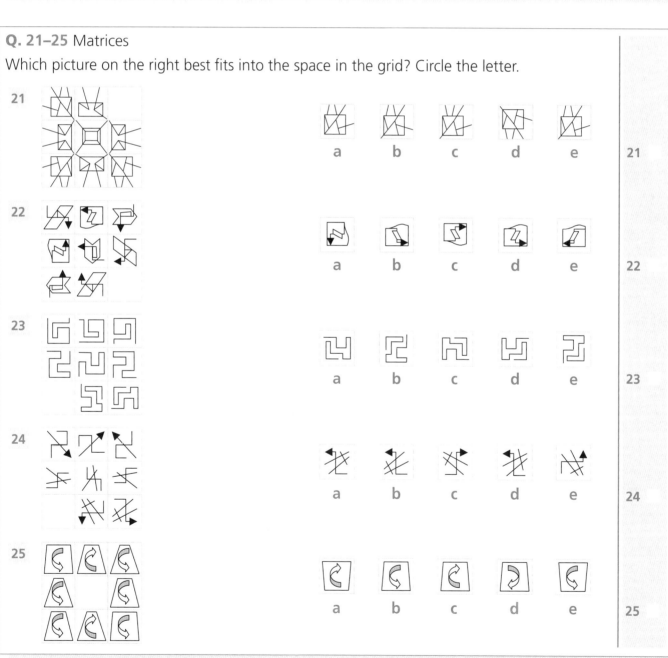

a   b   c   d   e   21

a   b   c   d   e   22

a   b   c   d   e   23

a   b   c   d   e   24

a   b   c   d   e   25

MARK

MARK
✓ OR ✗

Q. 26–30 Codes

What is the code of the final picture? Circle the letter.

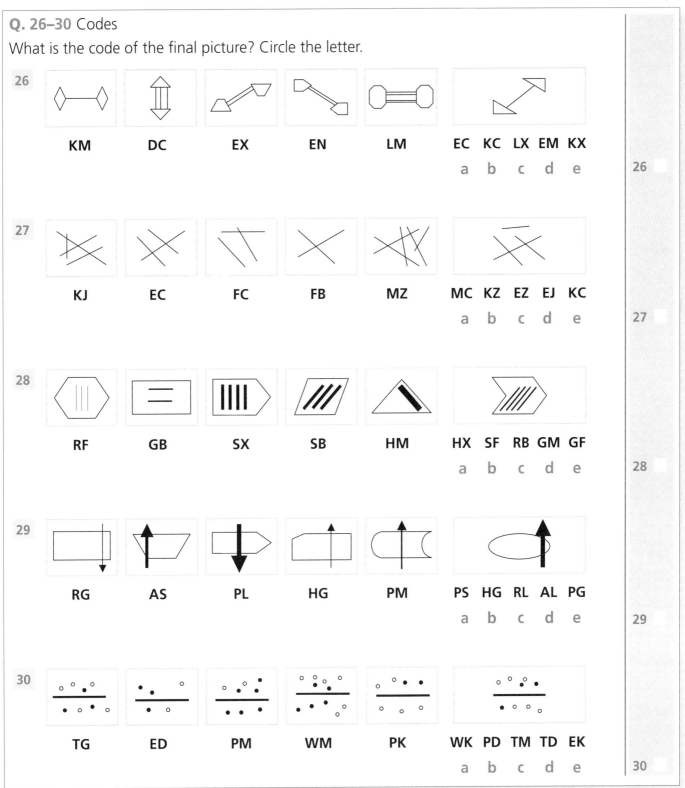

26

KM   DC   EX   EN   LM   EC KC LX EM KX
                                  a   b   c   d   e

26

27

KJ   EC   FC   FB   MZ   MC KZ EZ EJ KC
                                  a   b   c   d   e

27

28

RF   GB   SX   SB   HM   HX SF RB GM GF
                                  a   b   c   d   e

28

29

RG   AS   PL   HG   PM   PS HG RL AL PG
                                  a   b   c   d   e

29

30

TG   ED   PM   WM   PK   WK PD TM TD EK
                                  a   b   c   d   e

30

MARK

Q. 31–35 Combined pictures

Which picture on the right can be made by combining the first two pictures? Circle the letter.

31

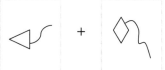

a   b   c   d   e   31

32

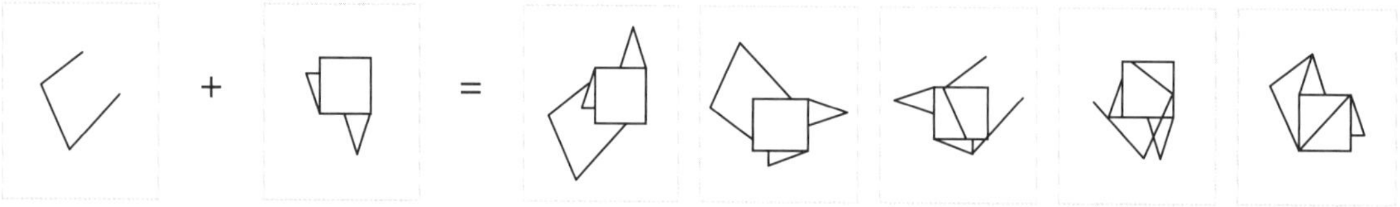

a   b   c   d   e   32

33

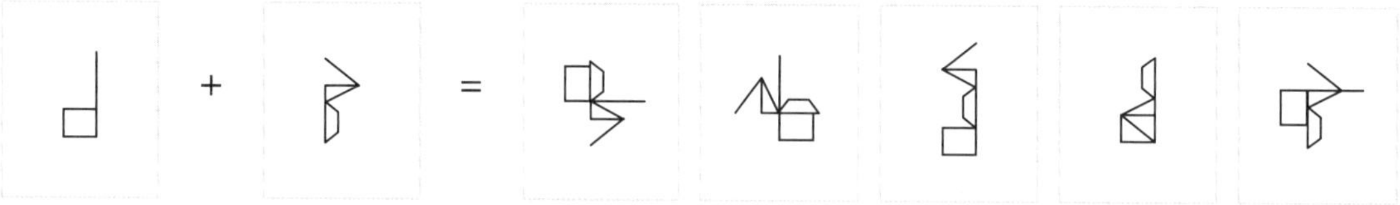

a   b   c   d   e   33

34

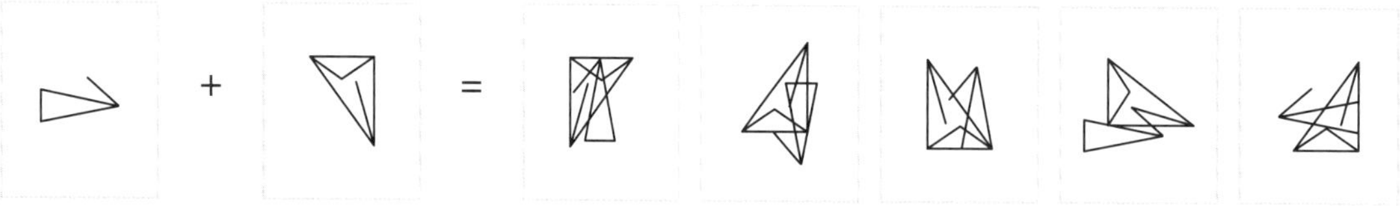

a   b   c   d   e   34

35

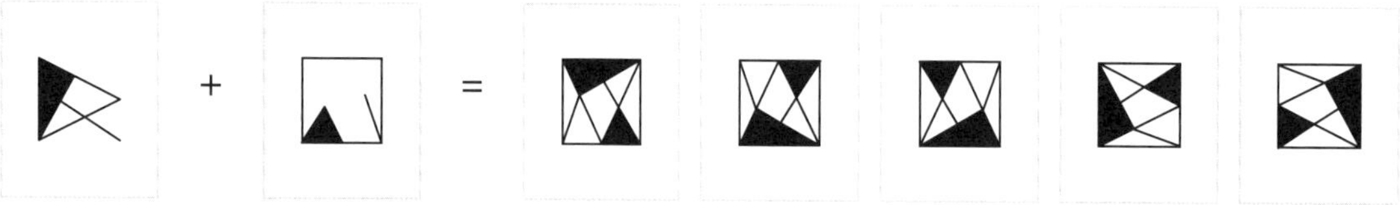

a   b   c   d   e   35

MARK

Q. 36–40 Nets of cubes

Which net can be made exactly from the cube? Circle the letter.

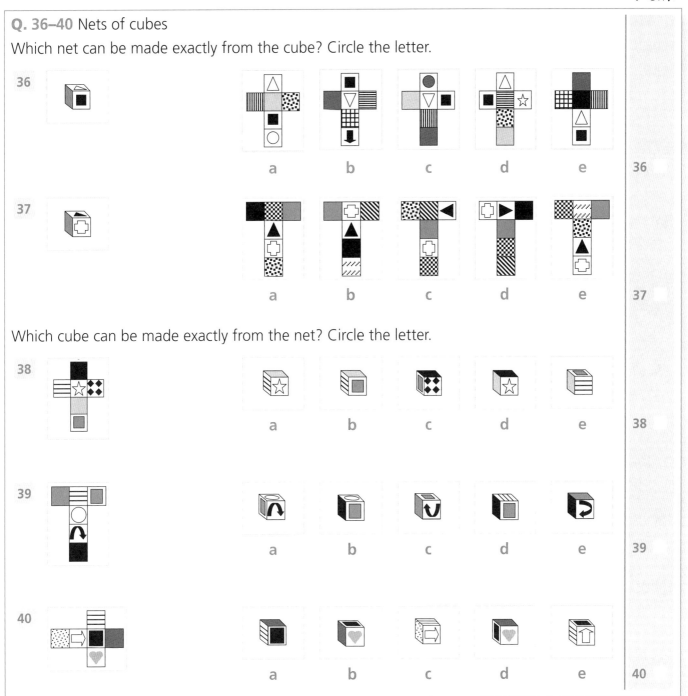

	36
	37
	38
	39
	40

MARK

MARK
✓ OR ✗

Q. 41–45 Series

Which picture on the right fits in the empty space? Circle the letter.

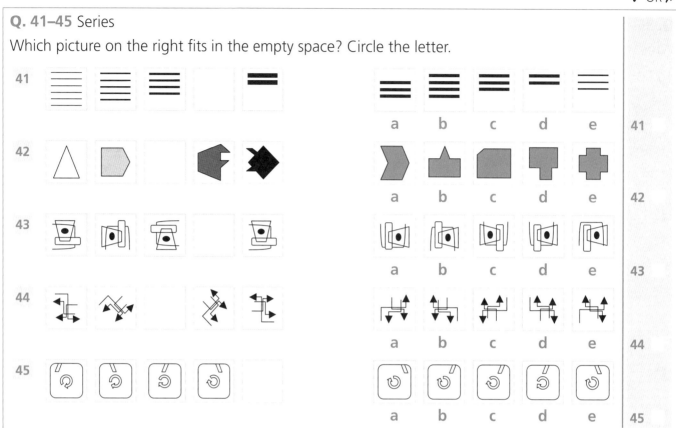

a   b   c   d   e   41

a   b   c   d   e   42

a   b   c   d   e   43

a   b   c   d   e   44

a   b   c   d   e   45

Q. 46–50 Reflected pictures

Which picture on the right is a reflection of the picture on the left? Circle the letter.

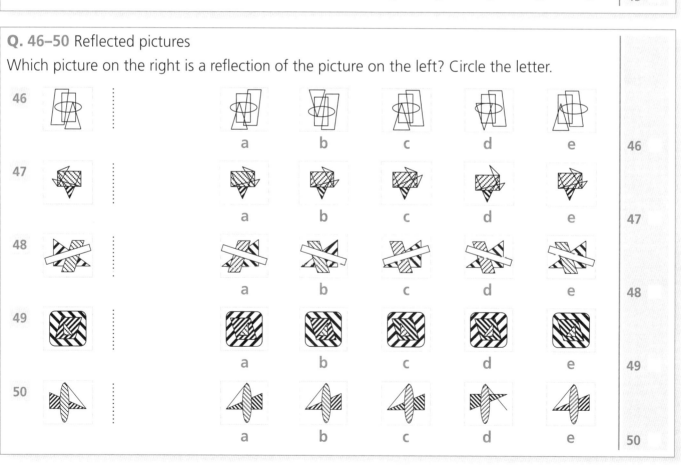

a   b   c   d   e   46

a   b   c   d   e   47

a   b   c   d   e   48

a   b   c   d   e   49

a   b   c   d   e   50

MARK

END OF TEST

PAPER 10 TOTAL MARK

START HERE

Q. 1–5 Odd ones out
Which picture is the odd one out? Circle the letter.

1

   a   b   c   d   e   1

2

   a   b   c   d   e   2

3

   a   b   c   d   e   3

4

   a   b   c   d   e   4

5

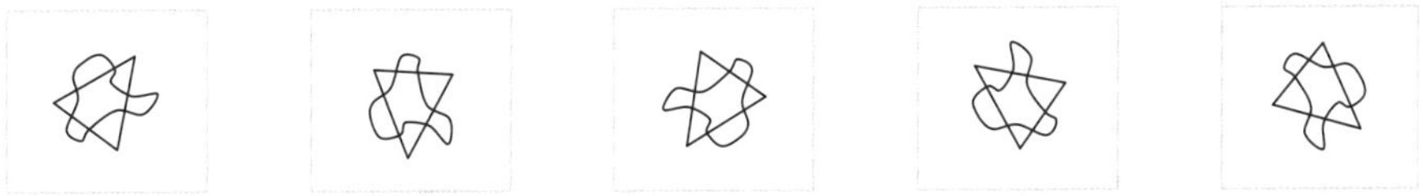

   a   b   c   d   e   5

Q. 6–10 Hidden pictures
In which picture on the right is the picture on the left hidden? Circle the letter.

6

                          a   b   c   d   e   6

7

                          a   b   c   d   e   7

MARK _____

MARK
✓ OR ✗

In which picture on the right is the picture on the left hidden? Circle the letter.

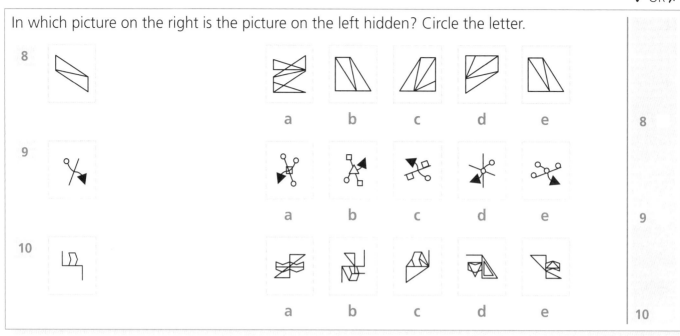

8   a   b   c   d   e   8

9   a   b   c   d   e   9

10   a   b   c   d   e   10

Q. 11–15 Analogies

Which of the five pictures on the right goes with the third one to make a pair like the two on the left? Circle the letter.

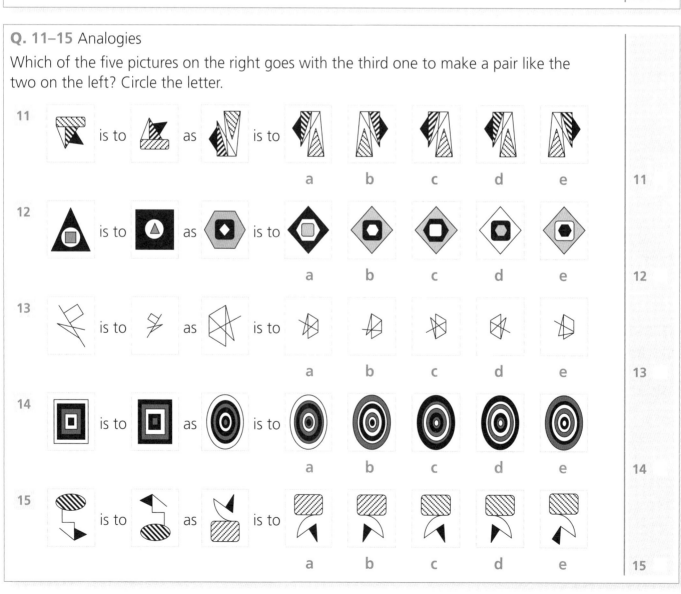

11   is to   as   is to   a   b   c   d   e   11

12   is to   as   is to   a   b   c   d   e   12

13   is to   as   is to   a   b   c   d   e   13

14   is to   as   is to   a   b   c   d   e   14

15   is to   as   is to   a   b   c   d   e   15

MARK

Non-verbal Reasoning
Progress Papers 2
Answers

Schofield&Sims

Non-verbal Reasoning Progress Papers 2

Notes for parents, tutors, teachers and other helpers

This pull-out book contains correct answers to all the questions in **Non-verbal Reasoning Progress Papers 2**, and is designed to assist you, the adult helper, as you mark the child's work. Once the child has become accustomed to the method of working, you may wish to give him or her direct access to this pull-out section.

When marking, put a tick or a cross in the tinted column on the far right of the question page. **Only one mark is available for each question**. Sub-total boxes at the foot of each page will help you to add marks quickly. You can then fill in the total marks at the end of the paper. The total score is out of 50 and can easily be turned into a percentage by multiplying the child's mark by two. (For example, a score of 40 multiplied by two gives 80%.) The child's progress can be recorded using the **Progress chart** on page 56.

The child should aim to spend between 45 and 75 minutes on each paper, but may need more time, or more than one session, to complete the paper. The child should try to work on each paper when feeling fresh and free from distraction.

How to use the pull-out answers

This answer booklet contains explanations and colour-coded pictures to help with marking. Where the child has answered a question incorrectly, take time to look at the question and answer together and work out how the correct answer was achieved.

By working through the tests and corresponding answers, the child will start to recognise the clues that he or she should look for next time. For example, the child may learn to analyse changes in pattern, reflection, rotation, size, colour and shape. These skills can then be put into practice by moving on to the next paper, as the difficulty increases incrementally throughout the series.

When a paper has been marked, notice if there are any topics that are proving particularly tricky. You may wish to complete some targeted practice in those areas, by focusing on that particular topic as it appears in each paper. For example, if a child has struggled with nets of cubes, but answered all other questions accurately, you may wish to target only nets of cubes questions in your next practice session. Each paper contains all 10 of the most common types of non-verbal reasoning question, so it is easy to tailor practice to the child's individual needs.

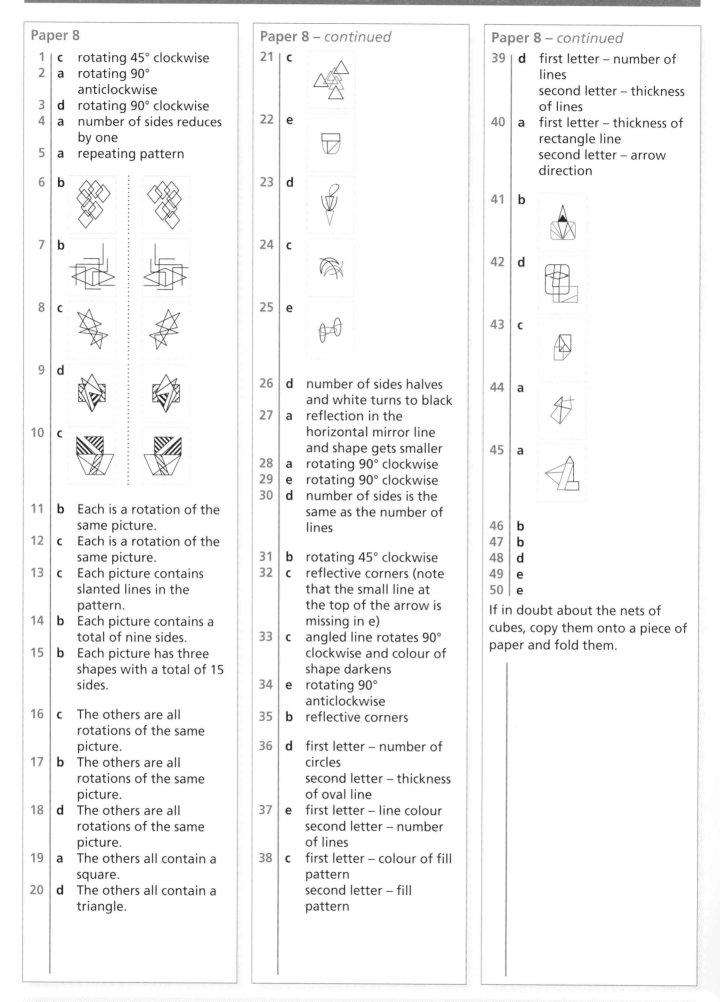

Paper 8

1 | c | rotating 45° clockwise
2 | a | rotating 90° anticlockwise
3 | d | rotating 90° clockwise
4 | a | number of sides reduces by one
5 | a | repeating pattern
6 | b |
7 | b |
8 | c |
9 | d |
10 | c |
11 | b | Each is a rotation of the same picture.
12 | c | Each is a rotation of the same picture.
13 | c | Each picture contains slanted lines in the pattern.
14 | b | Each picture contains a total of nine sides.
15 | b | Each picture has three shapes with a total of 15 sides.
16 | c | The others are all rotations of the same picture.
17 | b | The others are all rotations of the same picture.
18 | d | The others are all rotations of the same picture.
19 | a | The others all contain a square.
20 | d | The others all contain a triangle.

Paper 8 – *continued*

21 | c |
22 | e |
23 | d |
24 | c |
25 | e |
26 | d | number of sides halves and white turns to black
27 | a | reflection in the horizontal mirror line and shape gets smaller
28 | a | rotating 90° clockwise
29 | e | rotating 90° clockwise
30 | d | number of sides is the same as the number of lines
31 | b | rotating 45° clockwise
32 | c | reflective corners (note that the small line at the top of the arrow is missing in e)
33 | c | angled line rotates 90° clockwise and colour of shape darkens
34 | e | rotating 90° anticlockwise
35 | b | reflective corners
36 | d | first letter – number of circles
second letter – thickness of oval line
37 | e | first letter – line colour
second letter – number of lines
38 | c | first letter – colour of fill pattern
second letter – fill pattern

Paper 8 – *continued*

39 | d | first letter – number of lines
second letter – thickness of lines
40 | a | first letter – thickness of rectangle line
second letter – arrow direction
41 | b |
42 | d |
43 | c |
44 | a |
45 | a |
46 | b
47 | b
48 | d
49 | e
50 | e

If in doubt about the nets of cubes, copy them onto a piece of paper and fold them.

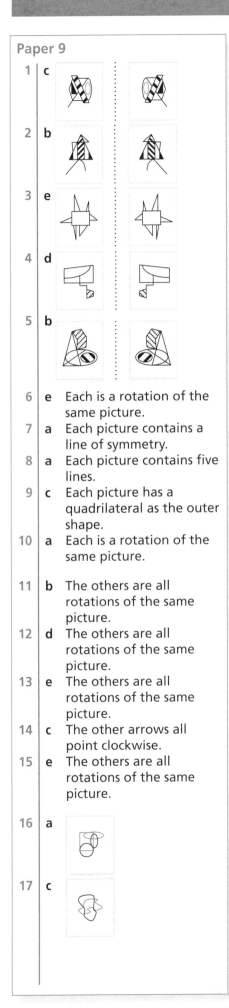

Paper 9

1 | c

2 | b

3 | e

4 | d

5 | b

6 | e | Each is a rotation of the same picture.
7 | a | Each picture contains a line of symmetry.
8 | a | Each picture contains five lines.
9 | c | Each picture has a quadrilateral as the outer shape.
10 | a | Each is a rotation of the same picture.

11 | b | The others are all rotations of the same picture.
12 | d | The others are all rotations of the same picture.
13 | e | The others are all rotations of the same picture.
14 | c | The other arrows all point clockwise.
15 | e | The others are all rotations of the same picture.

16 | a

17 | c

Paper 9 – continued

18 | a

19 | a

20 | c

21 | d | outer shape becomes the inner, middle shape becomes the outer, inner shape becomes the middle, grey shape turns white, black shape turns grey, white shape turns black
22 | c | the shape has one more side than the number of lines
23 | a | reflection in the vertical mirror line
24 | c | reflection in the vertical mirror line
25 | d | black turns white, grey turns black, white turns grey

26 | b | reflective corners
27 | c | rotating 90° clockwise, shape gets paler and smaller
28 | e | reflection in the horizontal mirror line
29 | d | rotating 45° anticlockwise
30 | b | rotating 90° clockwise

31 | a | first letter – outer line thickness
second letter – number of sides of outer shape
32 | a | first letter – number of sides
second letter – line style
33 | e | first letter – position of shorter line in relation to arrow head
second letter – arrow direction

Paper 9 – continued

34 | b | first letter – colour of internal shape
second letter – line direction
35 | d | first letter – number of sides
second letter – line thickness

36 | d

37 | b

38 | a

39 | c

40 | d

41 | e
42 | c
43 | d
44 | b
45 | d

If in doubt about the nets of cubes, copy them onto a piece of paper and fold them.

46 | b | rotating 45° clockwise, colour gets paler
47 | e | circle moves along rectangle to the right, colour of outer shape gets darker and internal lines rotate 45° anticlockwise
48 | b | rotating 90° anticlockwise
49 | c | number of right angles increases by two
50 | c | top triangle moves to the right and gets paler, bottom triangle moves to the left and gets darker, central line moves down and gets paler

Paper 10

1 | c | Each is a rotation of the same picture.
2 | d | Each picture contains an arrow bending clockwise.
3 | e | Each picture contains the same four shapes.
4 | c | Each is a rotation of the same picture.
5 | d | Each picture contains a curved shape.
6 | c | The others all have four line crosses.
7 | d | The others all have one less triangle on one side compared to the other.
8 | a | The others are all rotations of the same picture.
9 | d | The others are all rotations of the same picture.
10 | b | The others all have 14 right angles.
11 | b
12 | a
13 | b
14 | d
15 | e
16 | b | black turns white, white turns black and number of small shapes halves
17 | c | rotating 90° clockwise
18 | b | number of sides is divided by four
19 | a | number of sides doubles and number of shapes doubles

Paper 10 – *continued*

20 | b | reflection in the horizontal mirror line
21 | e | reflective corners (note that the small diagonal line at the bottom left corner is missing on a)
22 | d | same three shapes in each row and each shape rotates 90° clockwise as it moves rows
23 | d | rotating 90° anticlockwise
24 | a | rotating 90° anticlockwise
25 | c | arrow reflects in the horizontal mirror line, and the same three quadrilaterals appear in each row
26 | e | first letter – number of lines between the two end shapes
     second letter – direction of lines
27 | d | first letter – number of line crosses
     second letter – number of lines
28 | e | first letter – inner line thickness
     second letter – number of sides of outer shape
29 | c | first letter – position of arrow along shape
     second letter – line thickness of arrow
30 | d | first letter – number of circles under the line
     second letter – number of black circles under the line
31 | e
32 | e
33 | d

Paper 10 – *continued*

34 | c
35 | b
36 | b
37 | c
38 | b
39 | e
40 | e

If in doubt about the nets of cubes, copy them onto a piece of paper and fold them.

41 | c | number of lines reduces by one, the lines are all positioned at the top and their thickness increases
42 | b | number of sides increases by two and colour gets darker
43 | d | rotating 90° anticlockwise
44 | a | rotating 45° anticlockwise
45 | b | parallelogram reflects and moves along curved square, arrow rotates gradually clockwise
46 | c
47 | b
48 | d
49 | d
50 | c

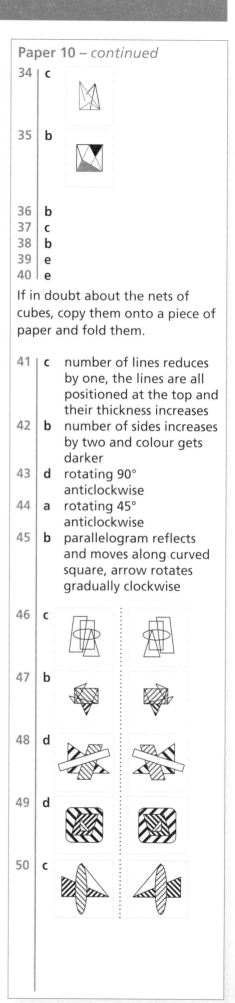

Paper 11

1	e	The others all contain a total of five circles.
2	a	The others are all rotations of the same picture (note that the smallest oval has no lines crossing it in **a**).
3	d	The others all have a trapezium with the wide end uppermost.
4	d	The others are all prisms with quadrilateral faces at both ends.
5	b	The others are all rotations of the same picture.
6	c	
7	d	
8	c	
9	d	
10	a	
11	a	reflection in the horizontal mirror line
12	b	outer shape becomes inner shape, inner shape becomes outer shape, colours stay in the same order
13	a	reflection in the vertical mirror line and shape becomes smaller
14	c	white turns black, black turns grey, grey turns white
15	b	rotating 180°

Paper 11 – *continued*

16	e	rotating 90° clockwise and getting smaller
17	e	rotating 90° anticlockwise and shapes getting darker
18	c	rotating 90° clockwise
19	b	reflective corners
20	e	rotating 45° clockwise
21	a	first letter – line direction of pattern second letter – number of sides
22	a	first letter – thickness of outer line second letter – number of sides
23	d	first letter – arrow thickness second letter – outer line style
24	c	first letter – total number of sides second letter – 'T' position
25	d	first letter – same shape (rotated) second letter – thickness of outer line
26	a	
27	c	
28	b	
29	e	
30	d	

Paper 11 – *continued*

31	a	
32	e	
33	a	
34	c	
35	c	

If in doubt about the nets of cubes, copy them onto a piece of paper and fold them.

36	e	rotating 90° clockwise
37	c	repeating pattern
38	d	rotating 90° anticlockwise
39	e	rotating 90° anticlockwise
40	a	rotating 90° anticlockwise
41	c	
42	d	
43	b	
44	d	
45	a	
46	a	Each picture contains two identical shapes.
47	b	Each is a rotation of the same picture.
48	c	Each picture contains a total of 15 sides.
49	a	Each is a rotation of the same picture.
50	a	Each is a rotation of the same picture (note position of star).

Paper 12

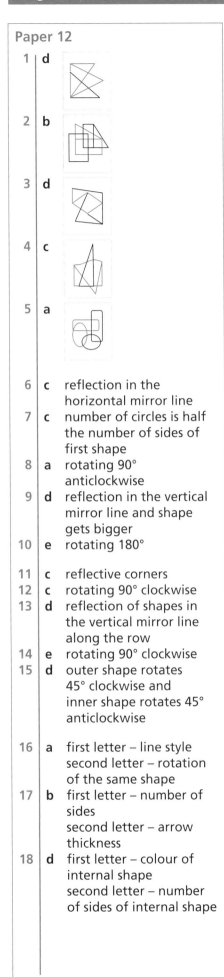

1 | d
2 | b
3 | d
4 | c
5 | a

6 | c | reflection in the horizontal mirror line
7 | c | number of circles is half the number of sides of first shape
8 | a | rotating 90° anticlockwise
9 | d | reflection in the vertical mirror line and shape gets bigger
10 | e | rotating 180°

11 | c | reflective corners
12 | c | rotating 90° clockwise
13 | d | reflection of shapes in the vertical mirror line along the row
14 | e | rotating 90° clockwise
15 | d | outer shape rotates 45° clockwise and inner shape rotates 45° anticlockwise

16 | a | first letter – line style
second letter – rotation of the same shape
17 | b | first letter – number of sides
second letter – arrow thickness
18 | d | first letter – colour of internal shape
second letter – number of sides of internal shape

Paper 12 – *continued*

19 | c | first letter – fraction of black rhombuses
second letter – total number of rhombuses
20 | e | first letter – number of sides of external shape
second letter – pattern of internal shape

21 | a
22 | a
23 | c
24 | b
25 | b

26 | c
27 | e
28 | c
29 | a
30 | c

If in doubt about the nets of cubes, copy them onto a piece of paper and fold them.

31 | a | circle moves right and gets darker, line moves left
32 | a | rotating 45° anticlockwise
33 | b | rotating 45° clockwise
34 | d | rotating 45° clockwise, triangle moves right along the rectangle and gets paler, line moves left along the rectangle
35 | e | rotating 90° anticlockwise

Paper 12 – *continued*

36 | b
37 | e
38 | a
39 | c
40 | c

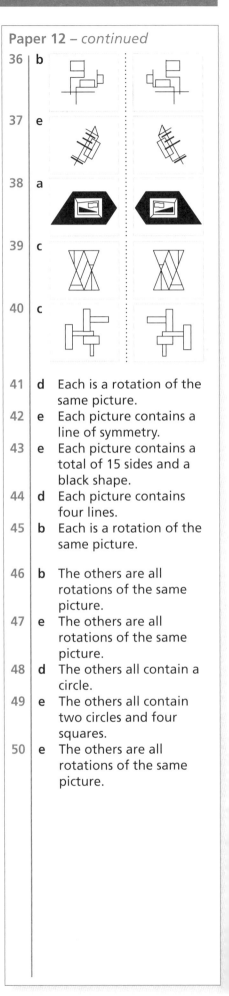

41 | d | Each is a rotation of the same picture.
42 | e | Each picture contains a line of symmetry.
43 | e | Each picture contains a total of 15 sides and a black shape.
44 | d | Each picture contains four lines.
45 | b | Each is a rotation of the same picture.
46 | b | The others are all rotations of the same picture.
47 | e | The others are all rotations of the same picture.
48 | d | The others all contain a circle.
49 | e | The others all contain two circles and four squares.
50 | e | The others are all rotations of the same picture.

Paper 13

1	d	rotating 90° anticlockwise
2	a	rotating 90° clockwise
3	d	reflection in the horizontal mirror line
4	b	rotating 180°
5	c	reflection in the vertical mirror line
6	a	rotating 90° clockwise
7	e	reflective corners
8	a	reflective corners
9	e	reflective corners
10	a	Each row contains one of each shape and the shapes rotate 90° anticlockwise on each row.
11	c	first letter – number of black circles second letter – total number of circles
12	a	first letter – direction of internal lines second letter – direction of single line
13	e	first letter – number of triangles above the line second letter – total number of triangles
14	c	first letter – colour of circles second letter – total number of circles
15	d	first letter – fill pattern second letter – direction of arrow/point
16	d	
17	b	
18	e	
19	d	
20	c	

Paper 13 – *continued*

21	b	
22	a	
23	e	
24	d	
25	d	

If in doubt about the nets of cubes, copy them onto a piece of paper and fold them.

26	c	colours move out from the centre
27	c	square number of circles
28	e	rotating 90° clockwise
29	a	star moves along the quadrilateral, quadrilateral gets paler, arrow reflects in the horizontal line: there will only be one point of the star on the quadrilateral
30	b	rotating 90° clockwise
31	c	
32	b	
33	d	
34	e	
35	b	

Paper 13 – *continued*

36	b	Each is a rotation of the same picture.
37	c	Each picture contains a black square.
38	c	The black and grey trapeziums have their wide edge facing out, if the shape were rotated so the grey trapezium were at the top, the white trapeziums would have both wide edges facing right.
39	d	Each picture contains a small square by a right angle.
40	c	Each is a rotation of the same picture.
41	b	The others are all rotations of the same picture.
42	e	The others are all quadrilaterals.
43	b	The others all have the circle in a right angle.
44	a	The others all contain a white rectangle and a grey rhombus.
45	d	The others all contain a circle in a left-hand corner.
46	a	
47	b	
48	c	
49	a	
50	b	

Paper 14

1 | e | rotating gradually anticlockwise
2 | d | rotating 90° anticlockwise
3 | d | rotating 90° anticlockwise and getting smaller
4 | a | reflective corners
5 | b | reflective corners
6 | c | first letter – direction of arrow/point
second letter – type of arrow
7 | d | first letter – number of circles above the arrow
second letter – direction of arrow
8 | a | first letter – number of white rectangles
second letter – direction of line
9 | c | first letter – colour or fill pattern of fourth rhombus
second letter – colour or fill pattern of second rhombus
10 | e | first letter – number of sides of outer shape
second letter – number of sides of internal shape
11 | a
12 | e
13 | a
14 | c
15 | b

Paper 14 – *continued*

16 | e
17 | c
18 | a
19 | b
20 | a

If in doubt about the nets of cubes, copy them onto a piece of paper and fold them.

21 | c | One line is added each time in the correct position.
22 | c | repeating pattern
23 | b | rotating 90° clockwise
24 | d | rotating 90° anticlockwise
25 | b | one less shape and number of sides decreases by one each time – shading gets gradually lighter
26 | e
27 | e
28 | d
29 | b
30 | e
31 | b | Each is a rotation of the same picture.
32 | e | Each picture contains a shape with only straight lines.
33 | e | Each picture has 12 sides, with one shape inside another shape.
34 | a | Each picture contains two lines crossing at right angles.

Paper 14 – *continued*

35 | d | Each is a rotation of the same picture.
36 | b | None of the others have any overlapping shapes.
37 | e | The others are all rotations of the same picture.
38 | e | The others all contain four lines.
39 | c | The others are all rotations of the same picture.
40 | b | The others are all rotations of the same picture (note position of the star).
41 | b
42 | d
43 | d
44 | c
45 | a
46 | b | number of sides halves and lines reflect in the vertical mirror line
47 | b | reflection in the horizontal mirror line
48 | e | number of lines is the same as the number of right angles
49 | a | number of sides doubles
50 | d | rotating 180°

This book of answers is a pull-out section from
Non-verbal Reasoning Progress Papers 2

Published by **Schofield & Sims Ltd**
Dogley Mill, Fenay Bridge, Huddersfield HD8 0NQ, UK
Telephone 01484 607080
www.schofieldandsims.co.uk

First published in 2016
This edition copyright © Schofield & Sims Ltd, 2018

Author: **Rebecca Brant**
Rebecca Brant has asserted her moral rights under the Copyright, Designs and
Patents Act, 1988, to be identified as the author of this work.

British Library Cataloguing in Publication Data
A catalogue record for this book is available from the British Library.

Design by **Oxford Designers & Illustrators**
Printed in the UK by **Page Bros (Norwich) Ltd**

ISBN 978 07217 1461 5

MARK
✓ OR ✗

Q. 16–20 Matrices

Which picture on the right best fits into the space in the grid? Circle the letter.

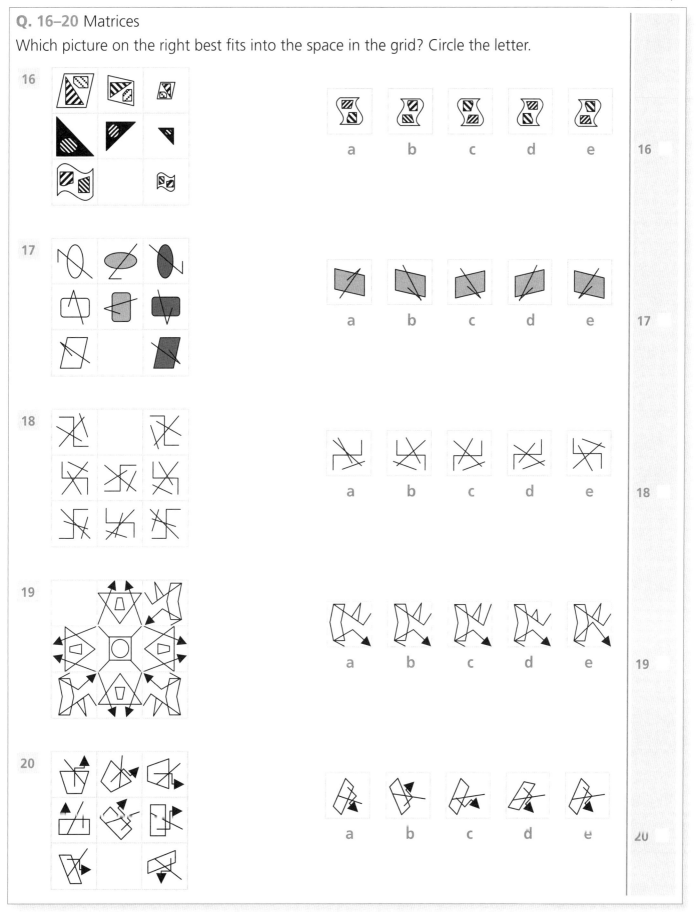

16

17

18

19

20

MARK

MARK
✓ OR ✗

Q. 21–25 Codes

What is the code of the final picture? Circle the letter.

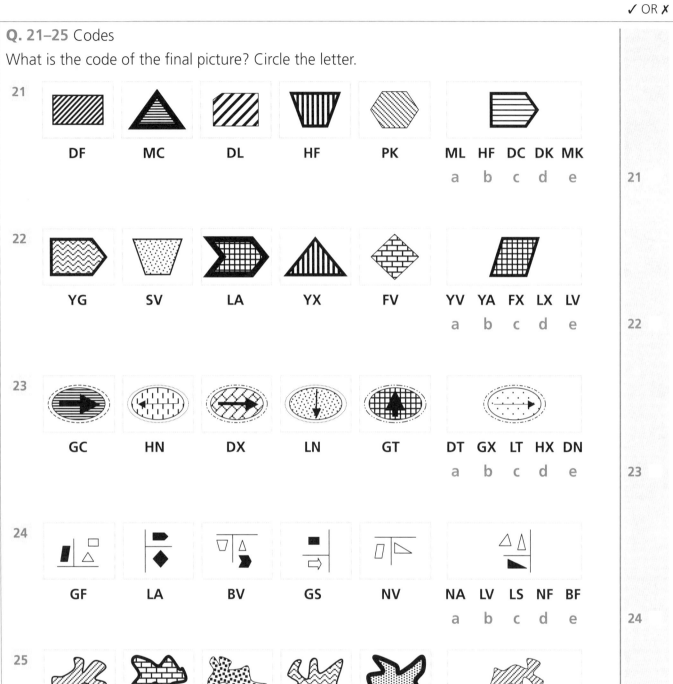

21

DF	MC	DL	HF	PK	ML HF DC DK MK
					a b c d e

21

22

YG	SV	LA	YX	FV	YV YA FX LX LV
					a b c d e

22

23

GC	HN	DX	LN	GT	DT GX LT HX DN
					a b c d e

23

24

GF	LA	BV	GS	NV	NA LV LS NF BF
					a b c d e

24

25

ZF	PG	DB	EF	PC	DF ZB PF EB EC
					a b c d e

25

MARK

MARK
✓ OR ✗

Q. 26–30 Combined pictures

Which picture on the right can be made by combining the first two pictures? Circle the letter.

26 + =

                a   b   c   d   e   26

27 + =

                a   b   c   d   e   27

28 + =

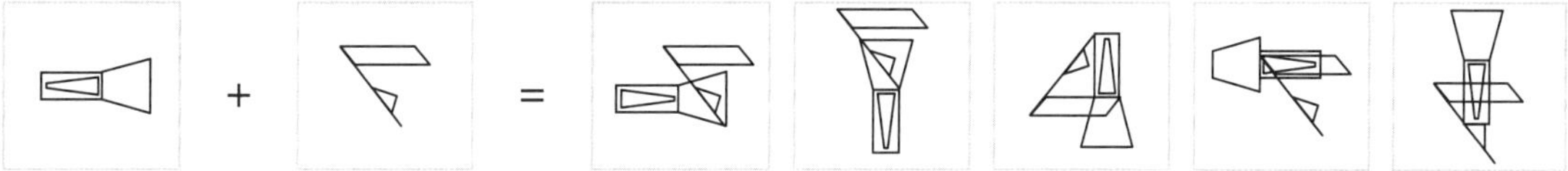

                a   b   c   d   e   28

29 + =

                a   b   c   d   e   29

30 + =

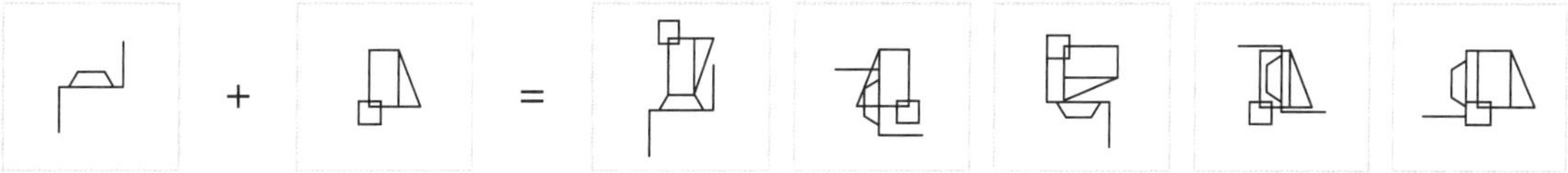

                a   b   c   d   e   30

Q. 31–35 Nets of cubes

Which net can be made exactly from the cube? Circle the letter.

31   

                a   b   c   d   e   31

32   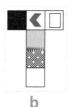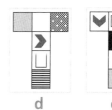

                a   b   c   d   e   32

MARK

MARK
✓ OR ✗

Which cube can be made exactly from the net? Circle the letter.

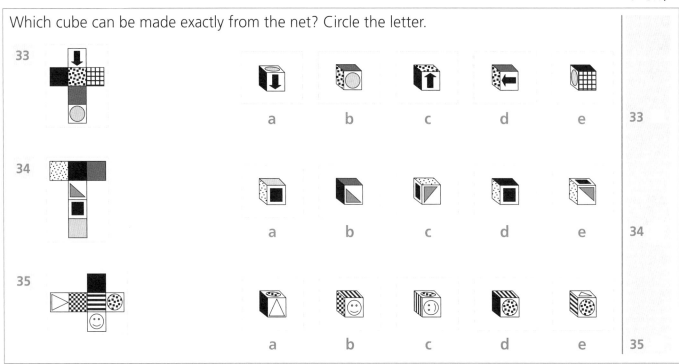

33   a   b   c   d   e   33

34   a   b   c   d   e   34

35   a   b   c   d   e   35

Q. 36–40 Series

Which picture on the right fits in the empty space? Circle the letter.

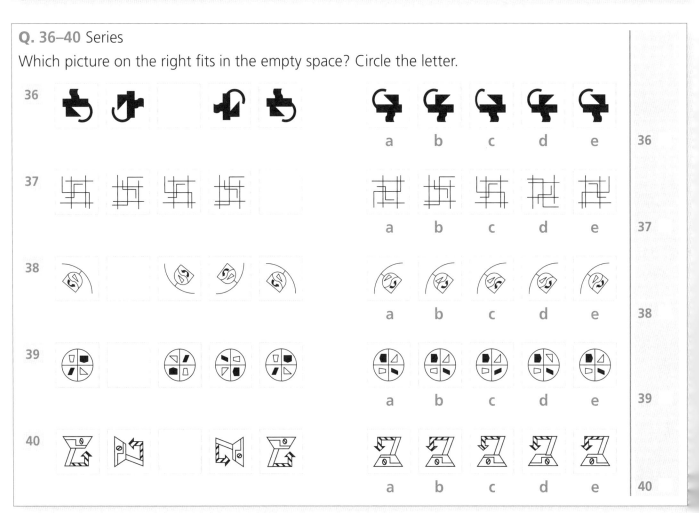

36   a   b   c   d   e   36

37   a   b   c   d   e   37

38   a   b   c   d   e   38

39   a   b   c   d   e   39

40   a   b   c   d   e   40

MARK

MARK
✓ OR ✗

Q. 41–45 Reflected pictures

Which picture on the right is a reflection of the picture on the left? Circle the letter.

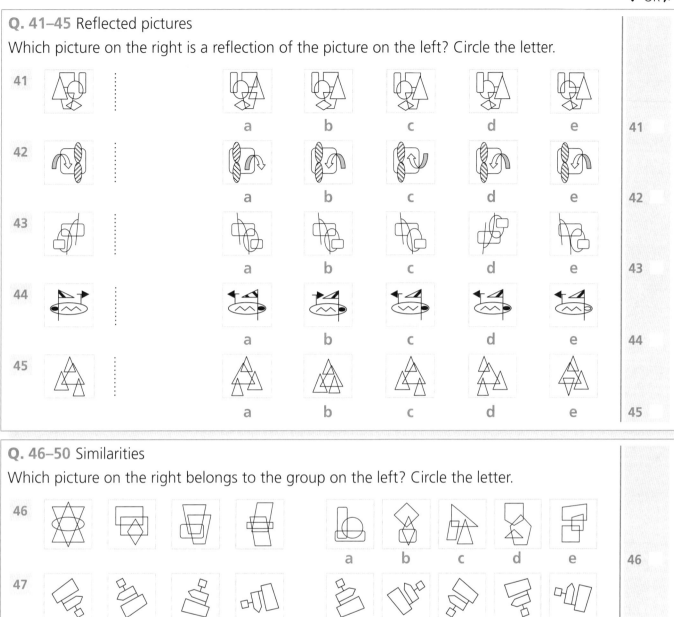

a	b	c	d	e

41 | 42 | 43 | 44 | 45

Q. 46–50 Similarities

Which picture on the right belongs to the group on the left? Circle the letter.

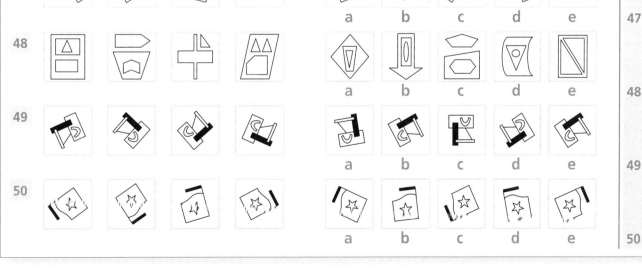

a	b	c	d	e

46 | 47 | 48 | 49 | 50

MARK

START HERE

Q. 1–5 Hidden pictures

In which picture on the right is the picture on the left hidden? Circle the letter.

1

     a   b   c   d   e   **1**

2

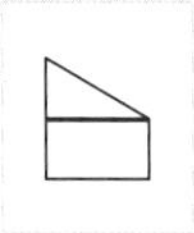

     a   b   c   d   e   **2**

3

     a   b   c   d   e   **3**

4

     a   b   c   d   e   **4**

5

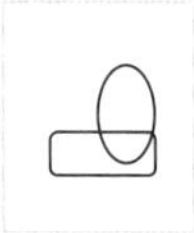

     a   b   c   d   e   **5**

Q. 6–10 Analogies

Which of the five pictures on the right goes with the third one to make a pair like the two on the left? Circle the letter.

6 is to  as  is to

     a   b   c   d   e   **6**

7 is to  as   is to

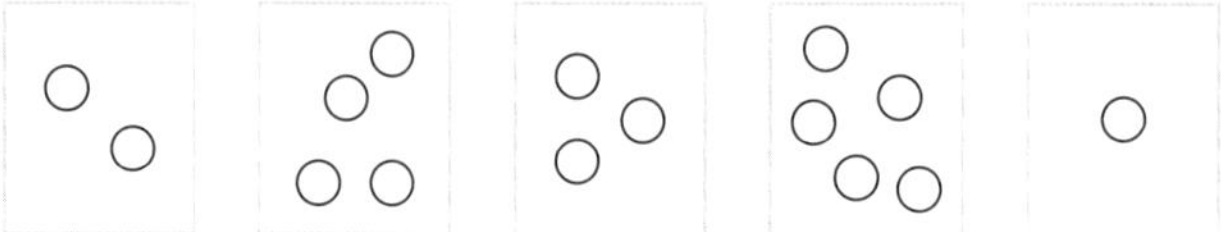

     a   b   c   d   e   **7**

8 is to 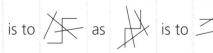 as   is to

     a   b   c   d   e   **8**

MARK

Schofield & Sims • Non-verbal Reasoning Progress Papers 2

MARK
✓ OR ✗

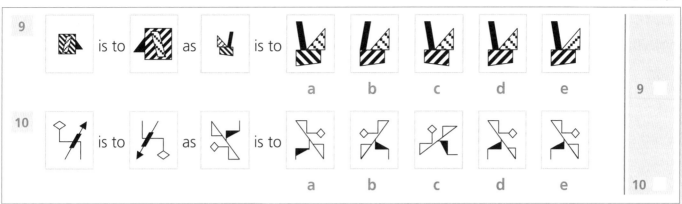

9

is to ___ as ___ is to

        a   b   c   d   e

9

10

is to ___ as ___ is to

        a   b   c   d   e

10

Q. 11–15 Matrices

Which picture on the right best fits into the space in the grid? Circle the letter.

11

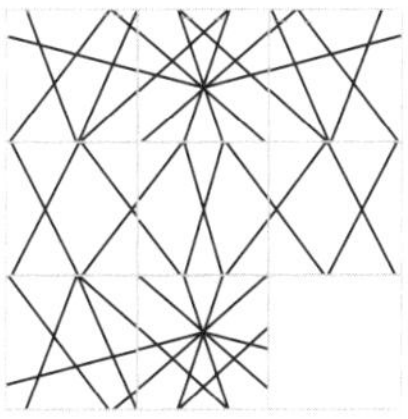

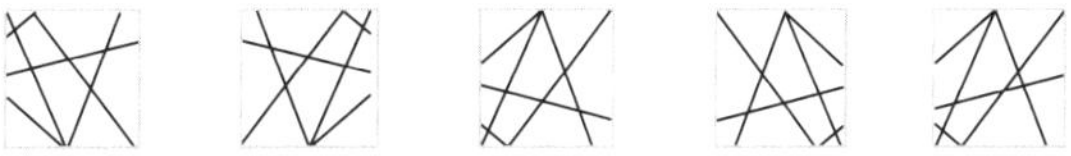

        a   b   c   d   e

11

12

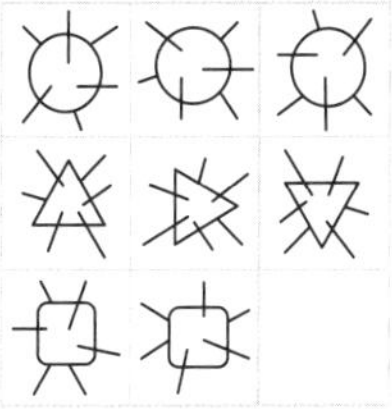

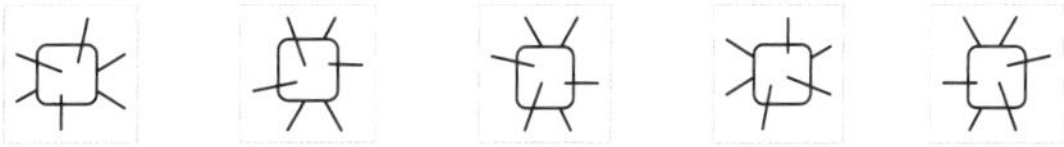

        a   b   c   d   e

12

13

        a   b   c   d   e

13

14

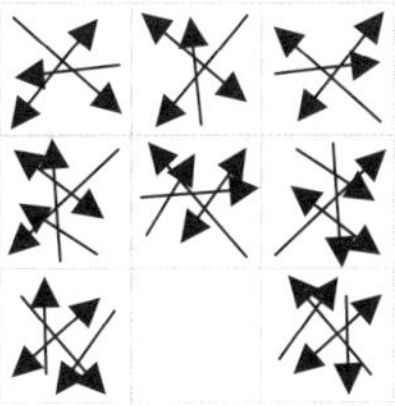

        a   b   c   d   e

14

15

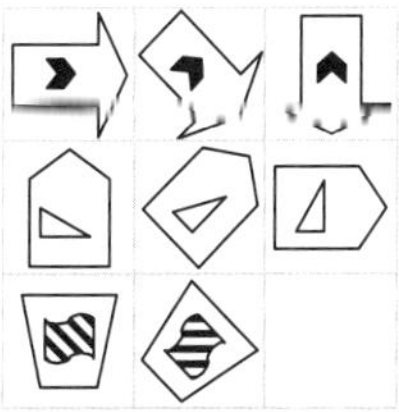

        a   b   c   d   e

15

MARK

MARK
✓ OR ✗

Q. 16–20 Codes

What is the code of the final picture? Circle the letter.

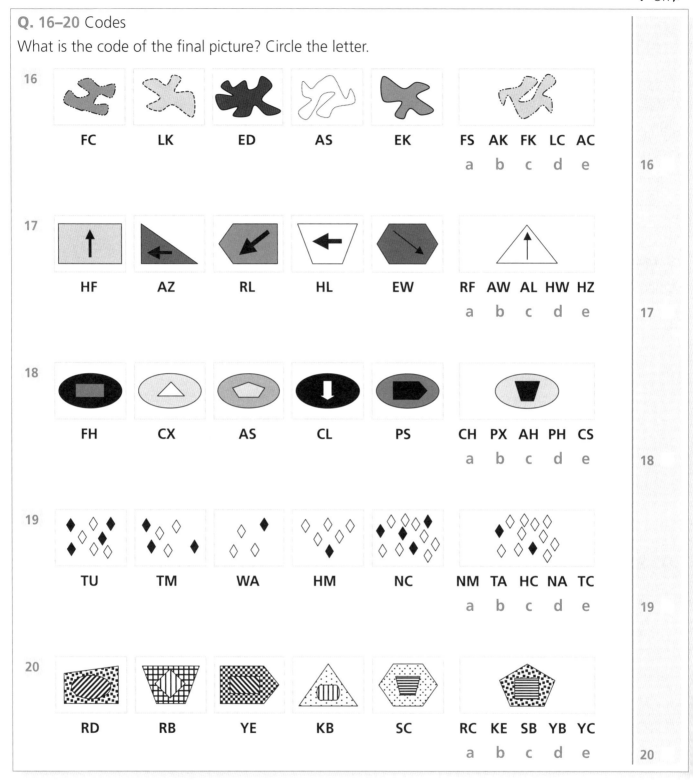

16

FC	LK	ED	AS	EK	FS AK FK LC AC
					a b c d e

16

17

HF	AZ	RL	HL	EW	RF AW AL HW HZ
					a b c d e

17

18

FH	CX	AS	CL	PS	CH PX AH PH CS
					a b c d e

18

19

TU	TM	WA	HM	NC	NM TA HC NA TC
					a b c d e

19

20

RD	RB	YE	KB	SC	RC KE SB YB YC
					a b c d e

20

MARK

MARK
✓ OR ✗

Q. 21–25 Combined pictures

Which picture on the right can be made by combining the first two pictures?
Circle the letter.

21 + =

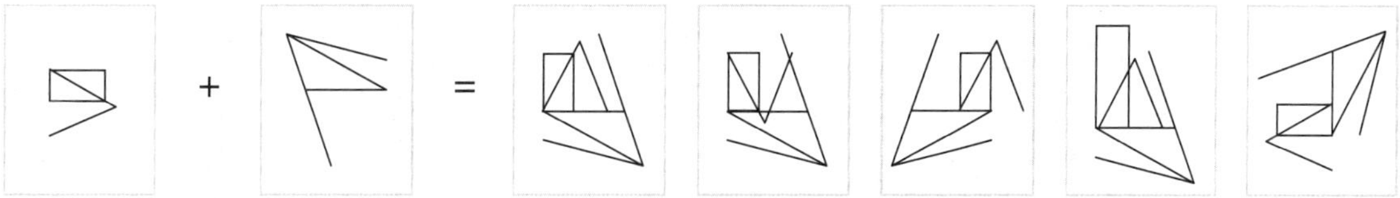

               a   b   c   d   e   21 ☐

22 + =

               a   b   c   d   e   22 ☐

23 + =

               a   b   c   d   e   23 ☐

24 + =

               a   b   c   d   e   24 ☐

25 + =

               a   b   c   d   e   25 ☐

MARK ☐

MARK
✓ OR ✗

Q. 26–30 Nets of cubes

Which net can be made exactly from the cube? Circle the letter.

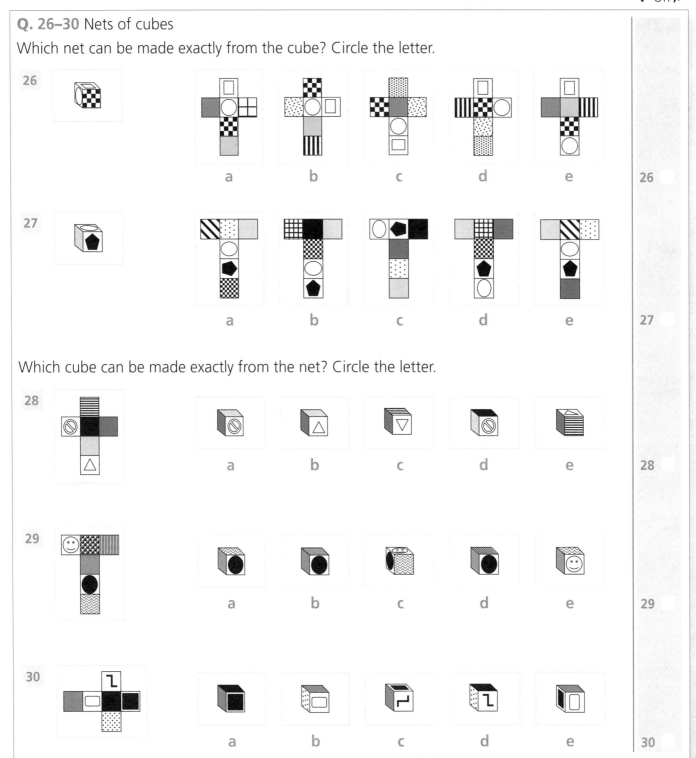

26   26
a   b   c   d   e

27   27
a   b   c   d   e

Which cube can be made exactly from the net? Circle the letter.

28   28
a   b   c   d   e

29   29
a   b   c   d   e

30   30
a   b   c   d   e

MARK

Schofield & Sims • Non-verbal Reasoning Progress Papers 2

MARK
✓ OR ✗

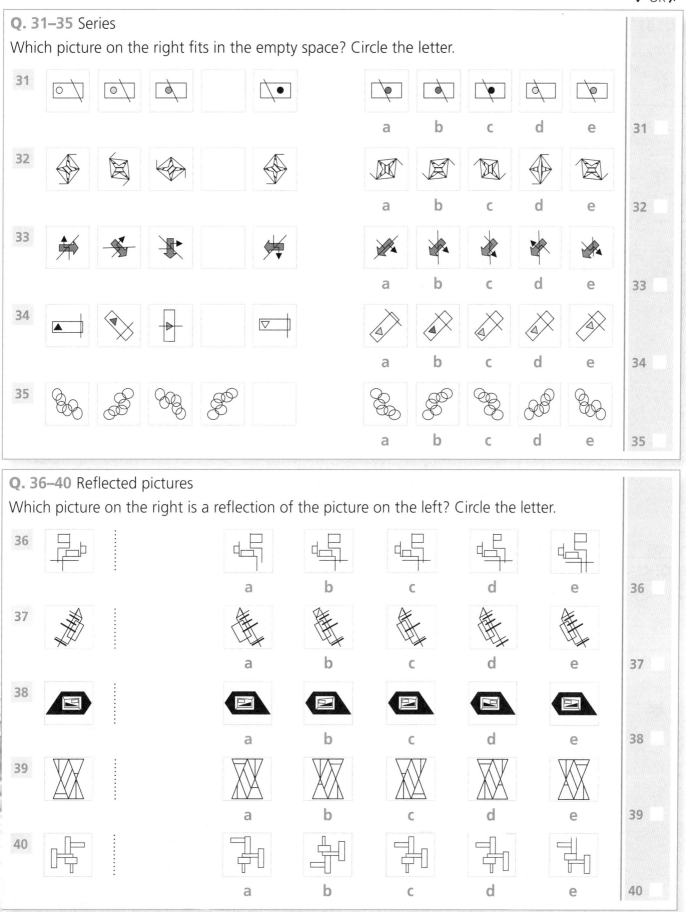

Q. 31–35 Series

Which picture on the right fits in the empty space? Circle the letter.

31 a b c d e 31

32 a b c d e 32

33 a b c d e 33

34 a b c d e 34

35 a b c d e 35

Q. 36–40 Reflected pictures

Which picture on the right is a reflection of the picture on the left? Circle the letter.

36 a b c d e 36

37 a b c d e 37

38 a b c d e 38

39 a b c d e 39

40 a b c d e 40

MARK

MARK
✓ OR ✗

Q. 41–45 Similarities

Which picture on the right belongs to the group on the left? Circle the letter.

41

          a   b   c   d   e   **41**

42

          a   b   c   d   e   **42**

43

          a   b   c   d   e   **43**

44

          a   b   c   d   e   **44**

45

          a   b   c   d   e   **45**

Q. 46–50 Odd ones out

Which picture is the odd one out? Circle the letter.

46   **49**

    a   b   c   d   e   a   b   c   d   e   **46**

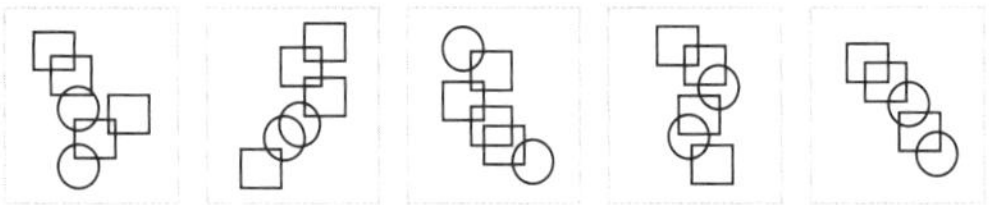

47   **50**

    a   b   c   d   e   a   b   c   d   e   **47**

48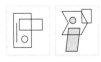

    a   b   c   d   e   **48**

                                                               49

                                                               50

MARK

END OF TEST

PAPER 12 TOTAL MARK

START HERE

Q. 1–5 Analogies

Which of the five pictures on the right goes with the third one to make a pair like the two on the left? Circle the letter.

1 is to as is to

a   b   c   d   e   1 ☐

2 is to as is to

a   b   c   d   e   2 ☐

3 is to as is to

a   b   c   d   e   3 ☐

4 is to as is to

a   b   c   d   e   4 ☐

5 is to as is to

a   b   c   d   e   5 ☐

Q. 6–10 Matrices

Which picture on the right best fits into the space in the grid? Circle the letter.

6 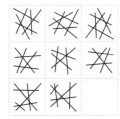

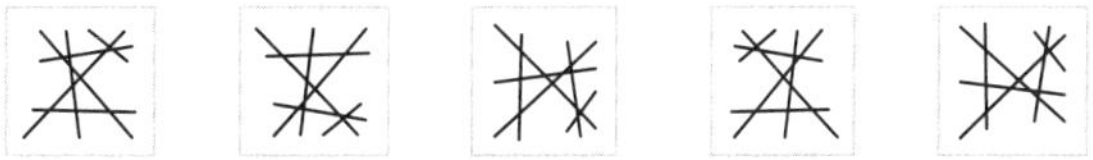

a   b   c   d   e   6 ☐

7 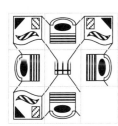

a   b   c   d   e   7 ☐

MARK ☐

MARK
✓ OR ✗

Which picture on the right best fits into the space in the grid? Circle the letter.

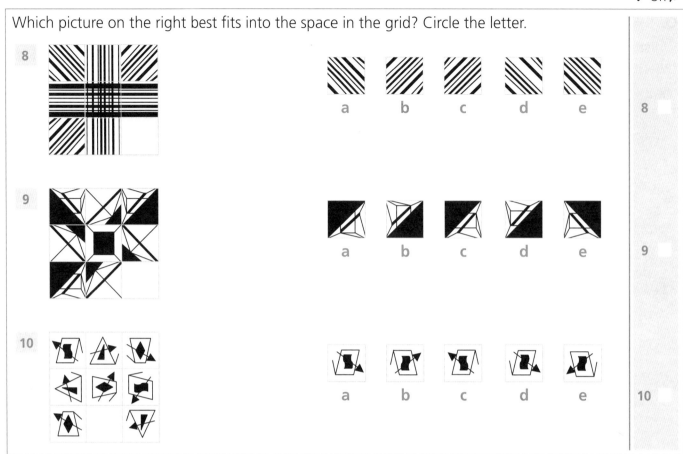

8   a   b   c   d   e   8

9   a   b   c   d   e   9

10   a   b   c   d   e   10

Q. 11–15 Codes

What is the code of the final picture? Circle the letter.

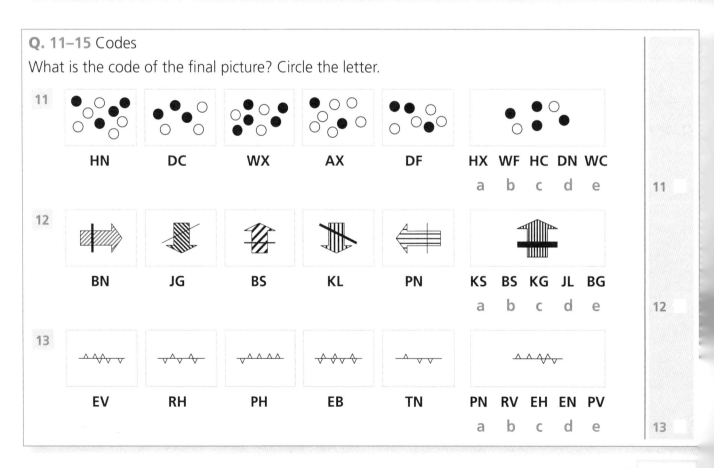

11   HN   DC   WX   AX   DF   HX   WF   HC   DN   WC
                                                       a   b   c   d   e   11

12   BN   JG   BS   KL   PN   KS   BS   KG   JL   BG
                                                       a   b   c   d   e   12

13   EV   RH   PH   EB   TN   PN   RV   EH   EN   PV
                                                       a   b   c   d   e   13

MARK

MARK
✓ OR ✗

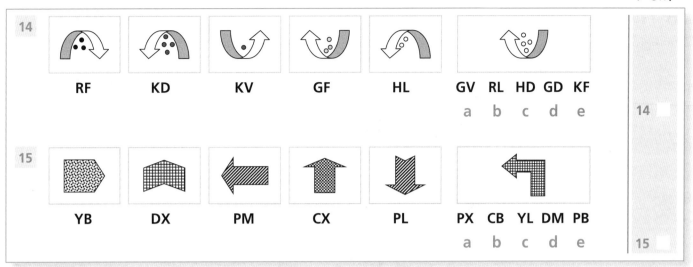

14

RF KD KV GF HL GV RL HD GD KF
a b c d e

14 ☐

15

YB DX PM CX PL PX CB YL DM PB
a b c d e

15 ☐

Q. 16–20 Combined pictures

Which picture on the right can be made by combining the first two pictures? Circle the letter.

16
 +  =
a b c d e

16 ☐

17
 + =
a b c d e

17 ☐

18
 + =
a b c d e

18 ☐

19
 + 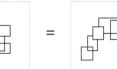 =
a b c d e

19 ☐

20
 + =
a b c d e

20 ☐

MARK ☐

MARK
✓ OR ✗

Q. 21–25 Nets of cubes

Which net can be made exactly from the cube? Circle the letter.

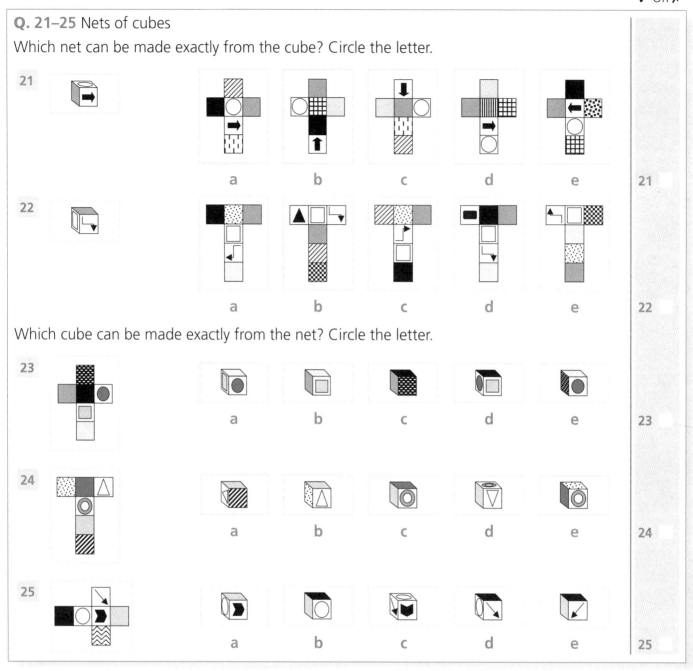

21   a   b   c   d   e | 21

22   a   b   c   d   e | 22

Which cube can be made exactly from the net? Circle the letter.

23   a   b   c   d   e | 23

24   a   b   c   d   e | 24

25   a   b   c   d   e | 25

Q. 26–30 Series

Which picture on the right fits in the empty space? Circle the letter.

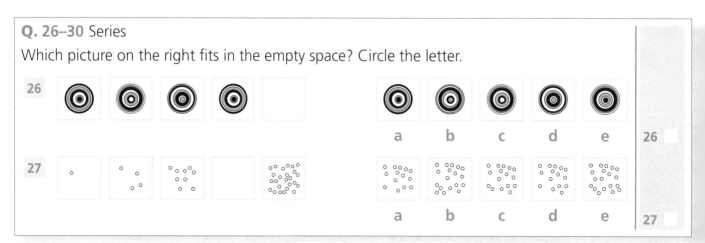

26   a   b   c   d   e | 26

27   a   b   c   d   e | 27

MARK

MARK
✓ OR ✗

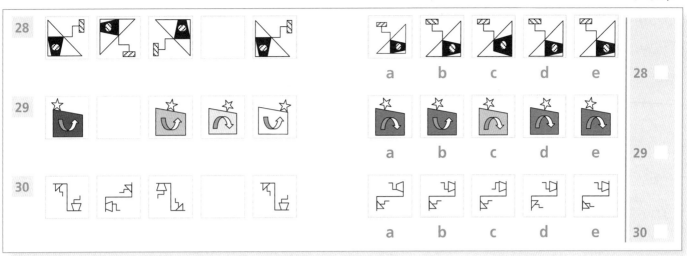

28   a   b   c   d   e   28 ☐

29   a   b   c   d   e   29 ☐

30   a   b   c   d   e   30 ☐

Q. 31–35 Reflected pictures

Which picture on the right is a reflection of the picture on the left? Circle the letter.

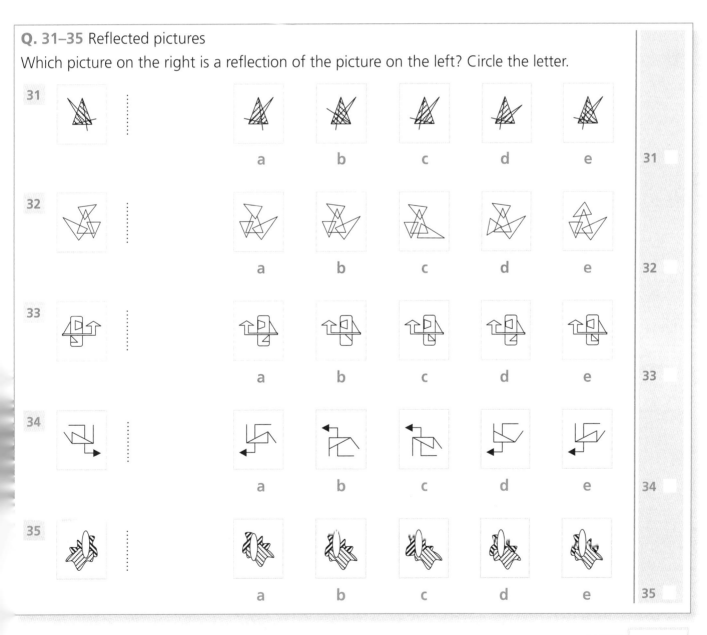

31   a   b   c   d   e   31 ☐

32   a   b   c   d   e   32 ☐

33   a   b   c   d   e   33 ☐

34   a   b   c   d   e   34 ☐

35   a   b   c   d   e   35 ☐

MARK ☐

MARK
✓ OR ✗

Q. 36–40 Similarities

Which picture on the right belongs to the group on the left? Circle the letter.

36

                            a   b   c   d   e   36

37

                            a   b   c   d   e   37

38

                            a   b   c   d   e   38

39

                            a   b   c   d   e   39

40

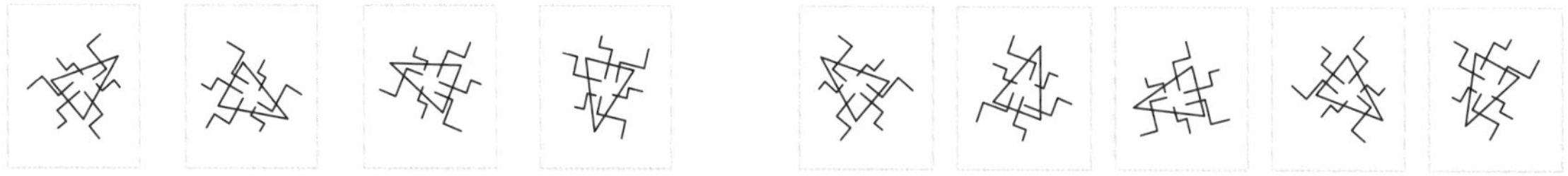

                            a   b   c   d   e   40

MARK

MARK
✓ OR ✗

Q. 41–45 Odd ones out

Which picture is the odd one out? Circle the letter.

41 
a   b   c   d   e

41 ☐

42 
a   b   c   d   e

42 ☐

43 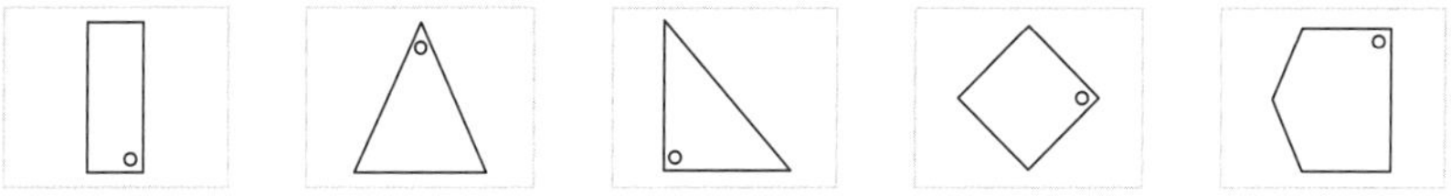
a   b   c   d   e

43 ☐

44 
a   b   c   d   e

44 ☐

45 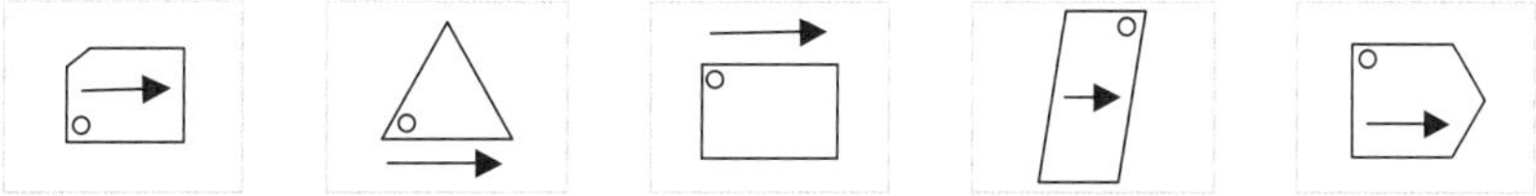
a   b   c   d   e

45 ☐

MARK ☐

MARK
✓ OR ✗

Q. 46–50 Hidden pictures

In which picture on the right is the picture on the left hidden? Circle the letter.

46
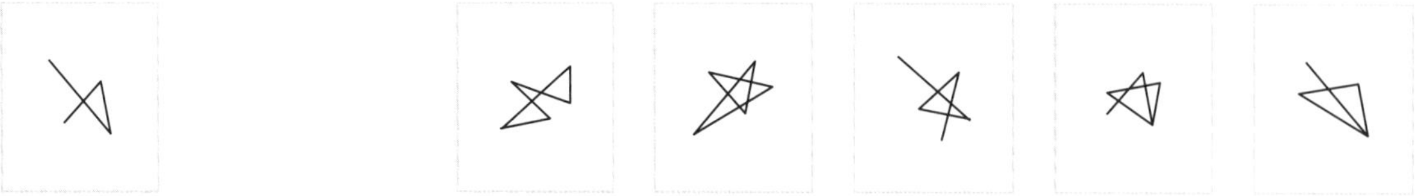
a b c d e 46

47
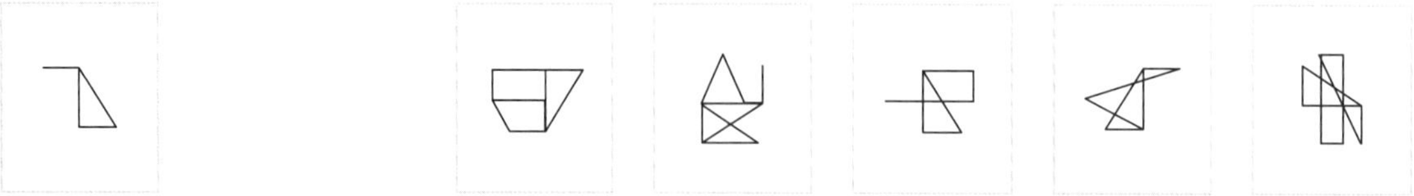
a b c d e 47

48
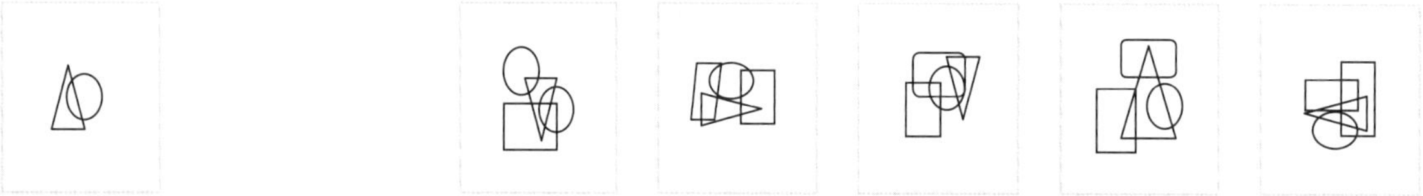
a b c d e 48

49
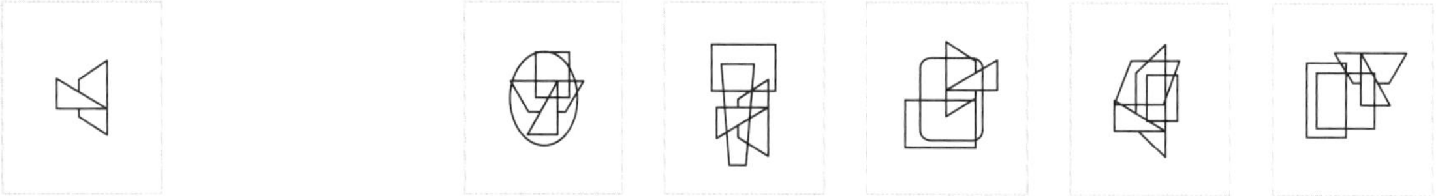
a b c d e 49

50
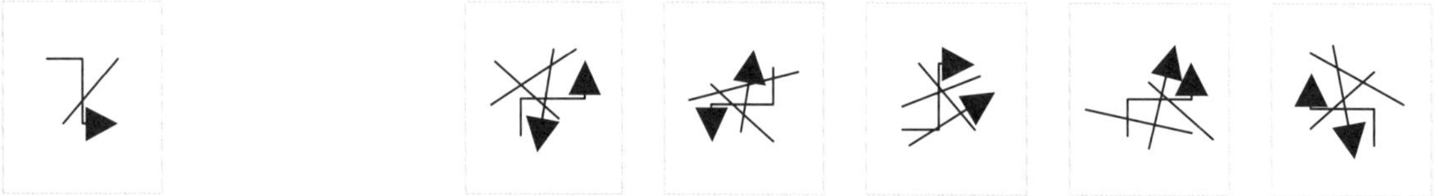
a b c d e 50

MARK

END OF TEST

PAPER 13 TOTAL MARK

START HERE

Q. 1–5 Matrices

Which picture on the right best fits into the space in the grid? Circle the letter.

1

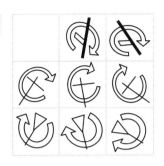

  a   b   c   d   e

1 ☐

2

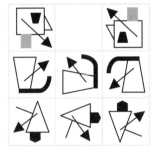

  a   b   c   d   e

2 ☐

3

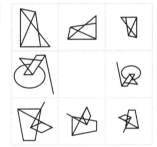

  a   b   c   d   e

3 ☐

4

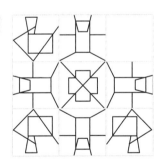

  a   b   c   d   e

4 ☐

5

  a   b   c   d   e

5 ☐

MARK ☐

MARK
✓ OR ✗

Q. 6–10 Codes

What is the code of the final picture? Circle the letter.

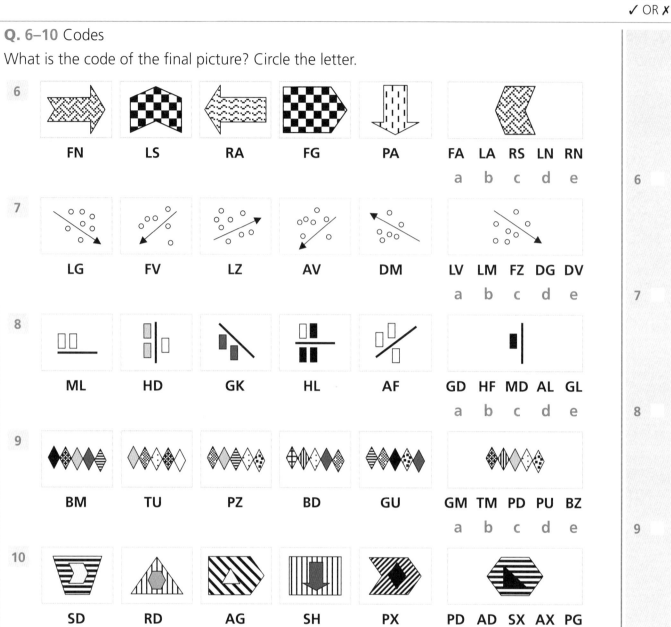

6

FN   LS   RA   FG   PA   FA   LA   RS   LN   RN
                                    a   b   c   d   e   **6**

7

LG   FV   LZ   AV   DM   LV   LM   FZ   DG   DV
                                    a   b   c   d   e   **7**

8

ML   HD   GK   HL   AF   GD   HF   MD   AL   GL
                                    a   b   c   d   e   **8**

9

BM   TU   PZ   BD   GU   GM   TM   PD   PU   BZ
                                    a   b   c   d   e   **9**

10

SD   RD   AG   SH   PX   PD   AD   SX   AX   PG
                                    a   b   c   d   e   **10**

Q. 11–15 Combined pictures

Which picture on the right can be made by combining the first two pictures? Circle the letter.

11

a   b   c   d   e   **11**

12

a   b   c   d   e   **12**

MARK

MARK
✓ OR ✗

Which picture on the right can be made by combining the first two pictures? Circle the letter.

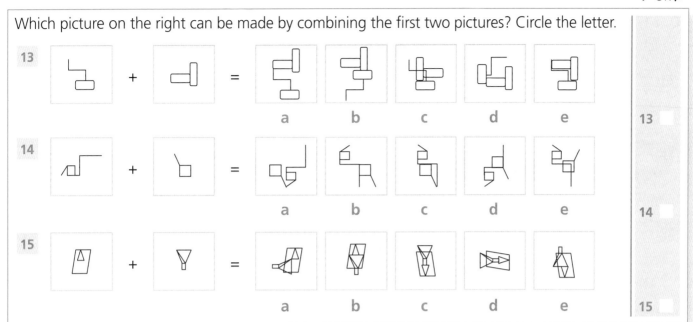

13

a   b   c   d   e   13 ☐

14

a   b   c   d   e   14 ☐

15

a   b   c   d   e   15 ☐

Q. 16–20 Nets of cubes

Which net can be made exactly from the cube? Circle the letter.

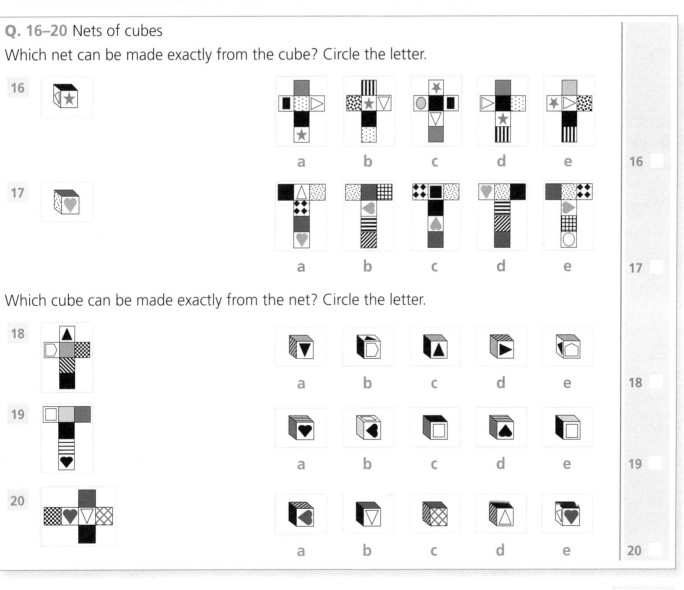

16

a   b   c   d   e   16 ☐

17

a   b   c   d   e   17 ☐

Which cube can be made exactly from the net? Circle the letter.

18

a   b   c   d   e   18 ☐

19

a   b   c   d   e   19 ☐

20

a   b   c   d   e   20 ☐

MARK ☐

MARK
✓ OR ✗

Q. 21–25 Series

Which picture on the right fits in the empty space? Circle the letter.

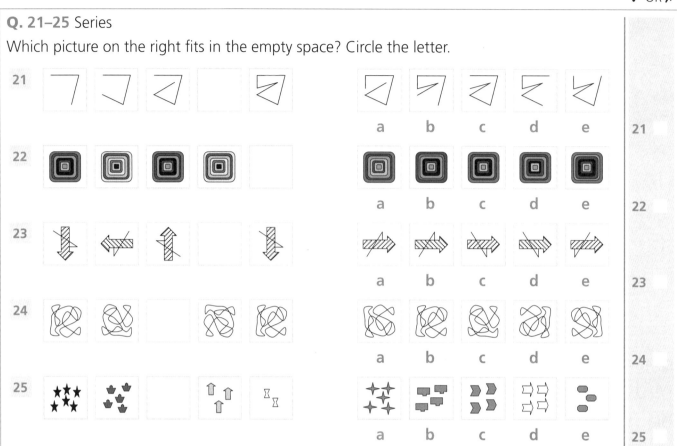

21   a   b   c   d   e   21

22   a   b   c   d   e   22

23   a   b   c   d   e   23

24   a   b   c   d   e   24

25   a   b   c   d   e   25

Q. 26–30 Reflected pictures

Which picture on the right is a reflection of the picture on the left? Circle the letter.

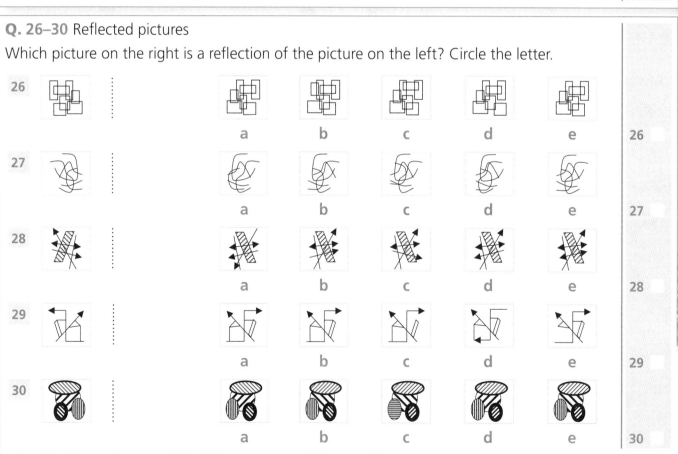

26   a   b   c   d   e   26

27   a   b   c   d   e   27

28   a   b   c   d   e   28

29   a   b   c   d   e   29

30   a   b   c   d   e   30

MARK

MARK
✓ OR ✗

Q. 31–35 Similarities

Which picture on the right belongs to the group on the left? Circle the letter.

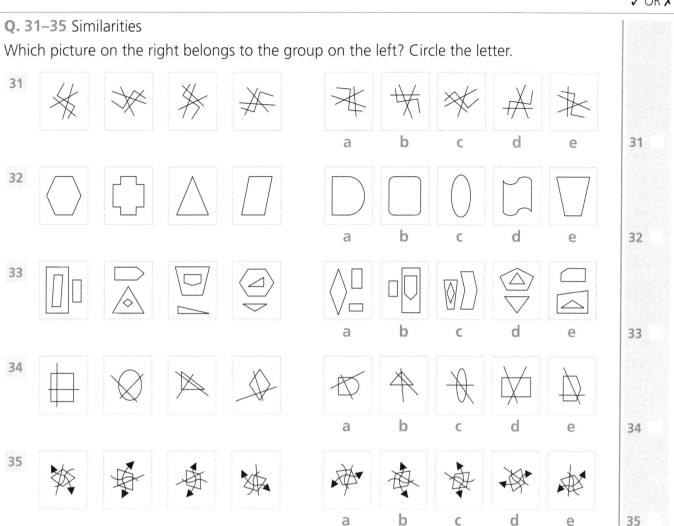

31	a	b	c	d	e	31
32	a	b	c	d	e	32
33	a	b	c	d	e	33
34	a	b	c	d	e	34
35	a	b	c	d	e	35

Q. 36–40 Odd ones out

Which picture is the odd one out? Circle the letter.

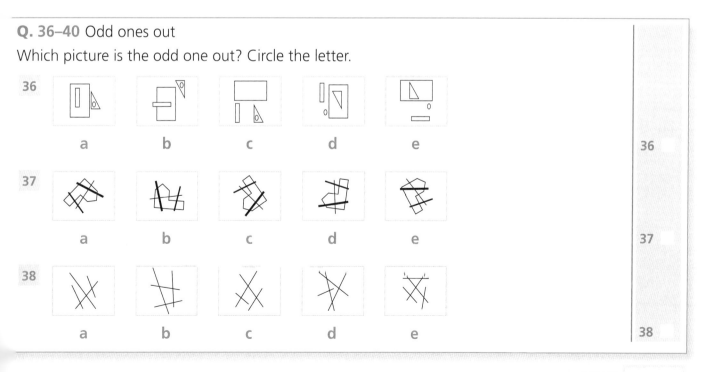

36	a	b	c	d	e	36
37	a	b	c	d	e	37
38	a	b	c	d	e	38

MARK

MARK
✓ OR ✗

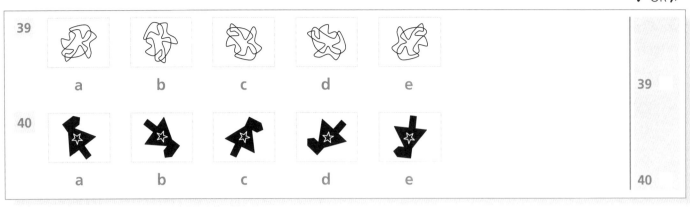

39   a   b   c   d   e   39

40   a   b   c   d   e   40

Q. 41–45 Hidden pictures

In which picture on the right is the picture on the left hidden? Circle the letter.

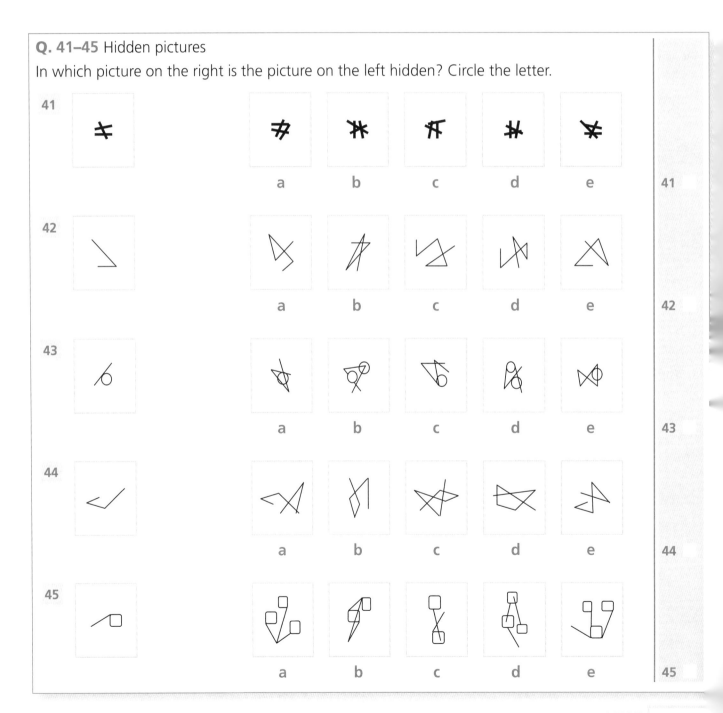

41   a   b   c   d   e   41

42   a   b   c   d   e   42

43   a   b   c   d   e   43

44   a   b   c   d   e   44

45   a   b   c   d   e   45

MARK

MARK
✓ OR ✗

Q. 46–50 Analogies

Which of the five pictures on the right goes with the third one to make a pair like the two on the left? Circle the letter.

46 is to as is to

    a   b   c   d   e   46

47 is to  as is to

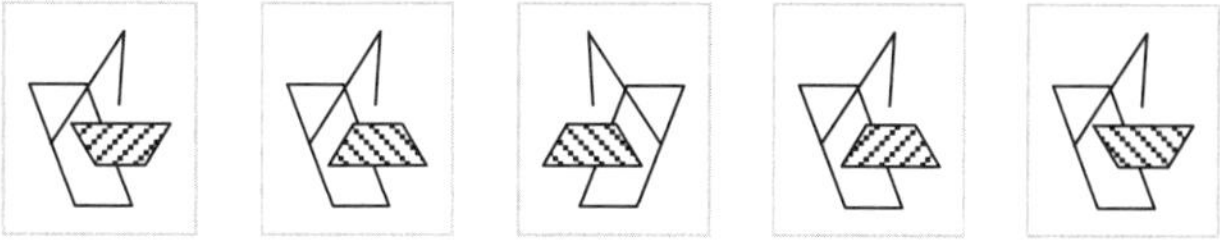

    a   b   c   d   e   47

48 is to as is to

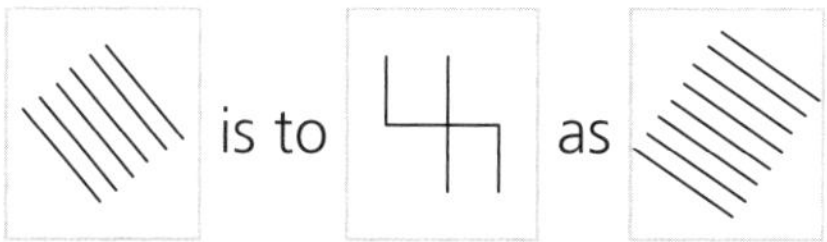

    a   b   c   d   e   48

49 is to as is to

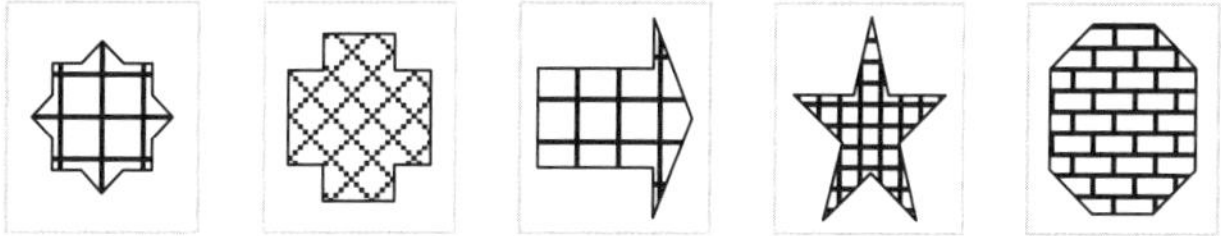

    a   b   c   d   e   49

50  is to as is to

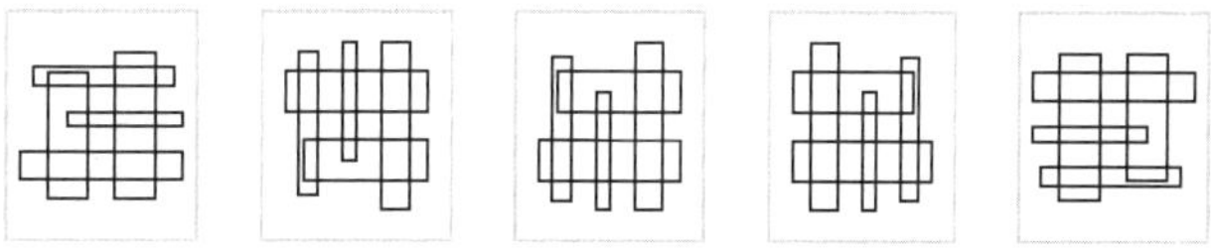

    a   b   c   d   e   50

MARK

PAPER 14 TOTAL MARK

END OF TEST

Progress chart

Write the score (out of 50) for each paper in the box provided at the bottom of the chart.
Then colour in the column above the box to the appropriate height to represent this score.

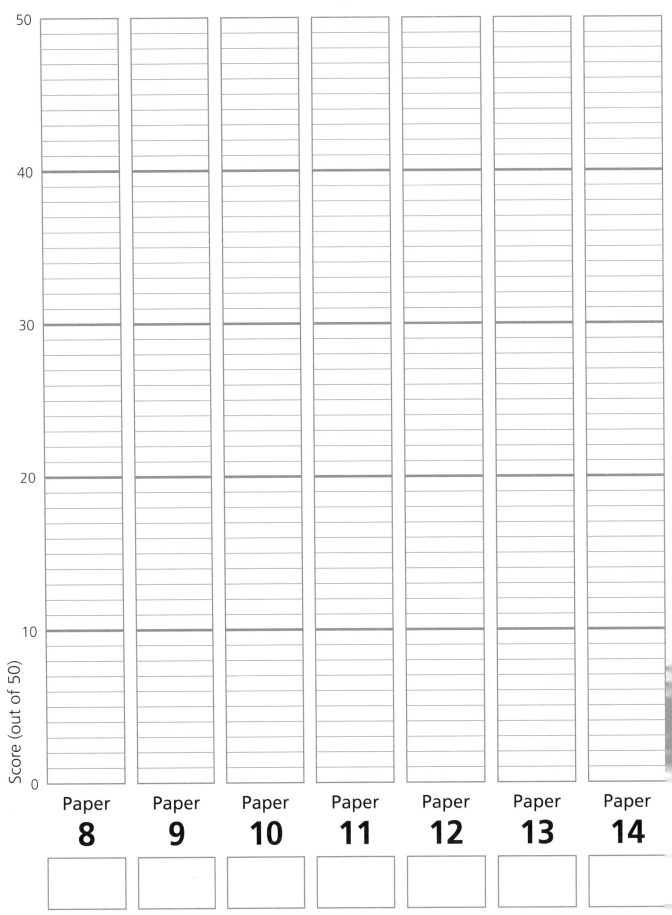